DEVELOPING MATH

C000132586

**Customisable
teaching resources
for mathematics**

HANDLING DATA

Ages 10–11

Helen Glasspoole

A & C Black • London

Contents

Introduction   4
Notes on the activities   6
Using the CD-ROM   12

Describe and predict outcomes from data using the language of chance or likelihood

Ferry times: 1 and 2   describe outcomes using the language of chance or likelihood   13–14
Chess guess: 1 and 2   predict outcomes using the language of chance or likelihood   15–16
Chance landing   predict outcomes using the language of chance or likelihood   17
Shady business   understand the language of chance and likelihood   18
More likely: 1 and 2   describe and predict outcomes using the language of chance or likelihood   19–20

Solve problems by collecting, selecting, processing, presenting and interpreting data, using ICT where appropriate; draw conclusions and identify further questions to ask

Finding out   solve problems by collecting and selecting data, using ICT where appropriate   21
Weather station   solve problems by collecting and selecting data, using ICT where appropriate   22
In conclusion: 1, 2, 3   interpret different representations of data, draw conclusions and identify further
and 4   questions to ask   23–26

Construct and interpret frequency tables, bar charts with grouped discrete data, and line graphs; interpret pie charts

Mike's and Spike's
bikes: 1 and 2   interpret frequency tables   27–28
Salad bar   complete and interpret a frequency table   29
Toolkit   construct and interpret a frequency table   30
Testing times   interpret a bar chart with grouped discrete data   31
Holiday time: 1 and 2   construct a bar chart with grouped discrete data   32–33
Computer scores   construct a bar chart with grouped discrete data   34–35
Stretchy statistics:
1 and 2   construct line graphs   36–37
Spotlight: 1 and 2   interpret line graphs   38–39
Deep blue sea: 1 and 2   construct and interpret line graphs   40–41
Miles to kilometres   interpret conversion graphs   42
You are what you eat   interpret pie charts   43
Hot 'n' tasty: 1 and 2   interpret pie charts   44–45
Plant sales: 1 and 2   interpret pie charts   46–47
Per 100 grams   interpret pie charts   48

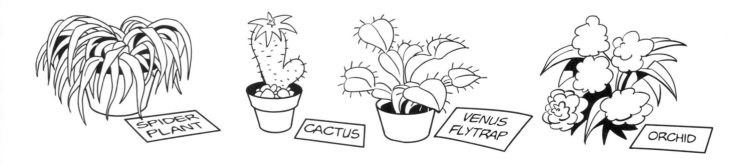

Describe and interpret results and solutions to problems using the mode, range, median and mean

Home on the range:

1 and 2	describe results using the range	**49–50**
Different modes:		
1 and 2	describe and interpret results and solutions using the mode	**51–52**
Paul's pool party	describe and interpret results and solutions using the mean	**53**
In the middle: 1 and 2	describe and interpret results and solutions using the median	**54–55**
Best average	compare the mean, mode and median for given sets of data	**56**
Side orders	describe and interpret results and solutions to problems using the mode, range, median and mean	**57**
Cheeky Chalky	solve problems involving mean, median, mode and range	**58**
Cube collection	describe and interpret results and solutions to problems using the mode, range, median and mean	**59**
Beijing 2008	describe and interpret results and solutions to problems using the range, median and mean	**60**

Resources

Blank line graph	**61**
Blank spinners	**62**
Answers	**63–64**

Published 2009 by A & C Black Publishers Limited
36 Soho Square, London W1D 3HB
www.acblack.com

ISBN 978-1-4081-0045-5

Copyright text © Helen Glasspoole 2009
Copyright illustrations © Kevin Hopgood 2009
Copyright cover illustration © Piers Baker 2009
Editors: Lynne Williamson and Marie Lister
Designed by Billin Design Solutions Ltd

The authors and publishers would like to thank Catherine Yemm and Judith Wells for their advice in producing this series of books.

A CIP catalogue record for this book is available from the British Library.

Printed and bound in Great Britain

A & C Black uses paper produced with elemental chlorine-free pulp, harvested from managed sustainable forests.

Introduction

100% New Developing Mathematics: Handling Data is a series of seven photocopiable activity books for children aged 4 to 11, designed to be used during the daily maths lesson. The books focus on the skills and concepts for Handling Data as outlined in the Primary National Strategy *Primary Framework for literacy and mathematics*. The activities are intended to be used in the time allocated to pupil activities in the daily maths lesson. They aim to reinforce the knowledge and develop the skills and understanding explored during the main part of the lesson, and to provide practice and consolidation of the learning objectives contained in the Framework document.

Handling Data

This strand of the *Primary Framework for mathematics* is concerned with helping pupils to develop the skills required to answer questions and solve problems by sorting and recording information according to certain given criteria and also criteria suggested by the children. In this strand they do this by recording in lists and tables and using practical resources, bar charts, bar-line and line graphs, and pie charts. Broadly speaking, this strand addresses topic areas that were described under the 'Handling Data' strand title of the former National Numeracy Strategy *Framework for teaching mathematics*.

Handling Data Ages 10–11 supports the teaching of mathematics by providing a series of activities to develop understanding of key concepts within the handling data cycle. The activities provide opportunities for children to develop the skills of collecting, organising, presenting, analysing and interpreting data. Children work with all types of graphs and charts, and pie charts are introduced. The language and key concepts of likelihood and chance linked to events and experiments are also used. Problems which involve finding the mode, mean, median and range of data are included. The following objectives are covered:

- describe and predict outcomes from data using the language of chance or likelihood;

- solve problems by collecting, selecting, processing, presenting and interpreting data, using ICT where appropriate; draw conclusions and identify further questions to ask;

- construct and interpret frequency tables, bar charts with grouped discrete data, and line graphs; interpret pie charts;

- describe and interpret results and solutions to problems using the mode, range, median and mean.

Extension

Many of the activity sheets end with a challenge (**Now try this!**), which reinforces and extends children's learning, and provides the teacher with an opportunity for assessment. These might include harder questions, with numbers from a higher range, than those in the main part of the activity sheet. Some challenges are open-ended questions and provide opportunity for children to think mathematically for themselves. Occasionally the challenge will require additional paper or that the children write on the reverse of the sheet itself. Many of the activities encourage children to generate their own questions or puzzles for a partner to solve.

Organisation

Very little equipment is needed, but it will be useful to have available: squared paper, graph paper, calculators, coloured pencils, dice, stop-watches, scissors and glue. You will also need a chess set for pages 15 and 20, and cubes for page 59.

Where possible, children's work should be supported by ICT equipment, such as software for drawing tables and charts on interactive whiteboards, data logging equipment or spreadsheet packages for computers. If possible, the children should also have access to the Internet. It is also vital that children's experiences are introduced in real-life contexts and through practical activities. The teachers' notes at the foot of each page and the more detailed notes on pages 6 to 11 suggest ways in which this can be done effectively.

To help teachers select appropriate learning experiences for the children, the activities are grouped into sections within the book. However, the activities are not expected to be used in this order unless stated otherwise. The sheets are intended to support, rather than direct, the teacher's planning.

Some activities can be made easier or more challenging by masking or substituting numbers. You may wish to re-use pages by copying them onto card and laminating them.

Accompanying CD

The enclosed CD-ROM contains all of the activity sheets from the book and a program that allows you to edit them for printing or saving. This means that modifications can be made to further differentiate the activities to suit individual pupils' needs. See page 12 for further details.

Teachers' notes

Brief notes are provided at the foot of each page, giving ideas and suggestions for maximising the effectiveness of the activity sheets. These can be masked before copying.

Further explanations of the activities can be found on pages 6 to 11, together with examples of questions that you can ask. Answers can be found on pages 63 and 64.

Whole-class warm-up activities

The following activities provide some practical ideas that can be used to introduce or reinforce the main teaching part of the lesson, or provide an interesting basis for discussion.

Asking the question

Encourage the children to refine their own or a given line of enquiry to a specific question. Give broad ideas with intentionally ambiguous language such as: *children watch too much television; older children are the fittest; we waste water; our school could be more environmentally friendly*. In pairs or small groups, the children discuss what would make a good question for the data to be collected.

Finding the average

Provide opportunities for the children to revise what is meant by 'mean', 'median' and 'mode'. Ask the children to find one of the averages in a range of different scenarios represented by different charts or graphs, as well as all three averages for the same set of data. Challenge the children to suggest which is the best/most meaningful average in a given situation and ask them to justify their viewpoints.

Proportion of pies

Present pie charts of different proportions with the same total to interpret and compare. Discuss the difference between/strengths and weaknesses of pie charts and bar graphs which both present discrete data. When the children are confident with the concept of a pie chart, present a pie chart with at least four sections. Give different totals that the data represents and challenge the children to find the value of each sector.

Practising scales

Linked to understanding and interpreting scales on a range of measuring instruments, ask the children to suggest appropriate scales for bar charts and line graphs. Ask questions such as: *If the tallest bar is 67, what do you think the scale should be? If the highest point on the line graph is 32, what divisions do you think the scale should be marked in?*

Possibilities

Ensure the children understand that probability based on likelihood can be informed by experience, 'normal' events and expected routines, for example: *What's the likelihood that it's going to snow today?* In contrast, probability based on chance events and outcomes can be calculated mathematically, for example: *What's the probability of pulling out a six from a pack of cards?* Use probability lines with the appropriate vocabulary to record and predict events.

Notes on the activities

Describe and predict outcomes from data using the language of chance or likelihood

In this section, the children address ideas of probability by focusing on the language that children use everyday. The children begin to use this language to describe and predict the outcomes of experiments. Encourage them to see that some outcomes are more likely than others, some are certain to happen, and some are impossible.

Ferry times: 1 and 2 (pages 13 and 14)

The timetable can be used to reinforce skills of reading charts and tables. The focus is on the likelihood of ferries leaving the jetty at the times given on the timetable. The children know that Mr Perry tries to stick to the timetable. This can be weighed up with experience, such as knowing that sometimes things happen for special occasions, or that transport will not keep to timetable if there are mechanical faults or there are lots of people getting on. This may affect some decisions around the use of 'very likely' and 'certain'. During the plenary, ask the children to justify their choices.

SUGGESTED QUESTIONS:

- How likely is it that a ferry will leave the jetty at midnight?
- What makes you think that it is very likely that a ferry will leave at 08:30 in the morning?

Chess guess: 1 and 2 (pages 15 and 16)

No knowledge of chess is needed for this activity, although it would be useful to have a chess set available so that all children are familiar with the number and name of each piece. Based on the number and colour of pieces, the children work out the probability of different pieces being chosen at random. Play a game of guessing or bingo with chess pieces first, so that children can get used to the chess pieces.

SUGGESTED QUESTIONS:

- Why do you think that picking a rook is more likely than picking a king?
- Which pieces are equally likely to be picked from the chess set?

Chance landing (page 17) and Shady business (page 18)

These two activities use spinners as a resource to generate data about chance. Page 62: Blank spinners can be used to reinforce and extend these concepts. The spinners are best copied onto card. Ensure that the children cut along the edges carefully so as not to affect which side the spinner lands on. Supervision might be needed when making the hole through the centre of the spinner.

SUGGESTED QUESTIONS:

- Why do you think that spinner is more likely to land on the shaded part?
- Can you shade the spinner so that it is twice as likely to land on blue than on red?

More likely: 1 and 2 (pages 19 and 20)

How to play the game

I In pairs or in small groups, the children cut out and shuffle the cards from pages 19 and 20.
I One player deals the cards so that each player has an equal number of cards.
I Each player places their cards in a pile face down on the table.
I Players turn over their top card and the player with the card that describes a 'more likely' event keeps the cards. If two events are equally likely, the cards are placed in the middle and picked up by the winner of the next round.
I The player with the most cards at the end of the game wins.

The children could add to the cards for this game by writing their own scenarios. The content is based on calculable outcomes, rather than likelihood – this could be the content of another game. The game cards could be copied onto thin card and laminated. As this game is intended to promote discussion, ensure that the children are free to challenge their opponent(s) – especially if mixed-ability children are working together.

SUGGESTED QUESTIONS:

- Explain why that situation is mathematically more probable than this one.
- Can you give me a situation that would be as equally likely as the one on this card?

Solve problems by collecting, selecting, processing, presenting and interpreting data, using ICT where appropriate; draw conclusions and identify further questions to ask

The handling data cycle always begins with a problem to be solved. It is important that children are given opportunities to decide for themselves how best to solve these problems. This involves considering what information is needed and how to collect it, for example surveys, experiments, questionnaires. The children then need to think about how they will organise the data that they collect.

Finding out (page 21)

This activity focuses on how to plan an investigation. Through paired discussions, the children should be encouraged to think about how data could be collected and how this could be done accurately. Concepts of average amounts and typical lengths of time can be linked to the mean average. The question relating to school population is more straightforward and could be attempted by less confident children first. Questions linked to topic work or local issues or environment could be substituted using the CD-ROM resource.

SUGGESTED QUESTIONS:

- How could you collect this data?
- How accurate do you think the data would be?

Weather station (page 22)

Building on previous/current work on the topic of 'weather', the children think about data that could be collected over a month/half a term. Examples might include: presence/absence of sun, rain, hail, snow, different types of cloud; amount of rain collected per day/week; force of wind; direction of wind (linked to compass work). The children plan and develop lines of enquiry to then collect, organise and represent information relating to their chosen area. Organise groups so that a range of data is collected. The children could then interpret results and review methods of data collection, suggesting improvements for another time. In groups, the children can identify related questions about their data for others in the class to answer.

SUGGESTED QUESTIONS:

- Is that a fair way to collect rainfall?
- How could you record the data to ensure it is accurate?

In conclusion: 1, 2, 3 and 4 (pages 23 to 26)

The children should work in pairs on these four activities. The focus of this activity is for the children to consider what the data does and does not tell the reader and, therefore, what conclusions can and cannot be drawn. The activity can also be used to encourage children to think about further lines of enquiry based on each set of data. The role of experience and preconceived ideas is also considered through statements such as 'Girls are better at football than boys', which may shape the way that the reader interprets the data.

SUGGESTED QUESTIONS:

- Why do you agree/disagree with that statement?
- Is it fair to draw that conclusion from this data?

Construct and interpret frequency tables, bar charts with grouped discrete data, and line graphs; interpret pie charts

Children will have had experience in constructing frequency charts, pictograms, bar charts and line graphs. They develop these skills to draw charts with a variety of scales, and continue to consider how to represent changes that take place over time. They are introduced to pie charts and begin to understand how these are used to represent data.

Mike's and Spike's bikes: 1 and 2 (pages 27 and 28)

These two worksheets require the children to interpret and compare data presented in frequency tables. Encourage the children to draw from real-life contexts when making conclusions about the two graphs showing sales of bikes and sales of bike lights. For example, the number of sales will depend on the weather, hours of darkness, Christmas and New Year sales.

SUGGESTED QUESTIONS:

- Which bike shop do you think makes the most money? Why do you think this?
- What other data could you collect from Mike and Spike?

Salad bar (page 29)

This activity reinforces the children's understanding of the use of a tally to collect data over time. The focus is on the total number of portions served for each salad type. As an extension, the children could organise the data for each day of the week to consider whether salad was a more popular choice on any particular day. Different aspects of this data could be represented on blank bar charts. It could also be used (with teacher support) to show proportions of totals using pie charts.

SUGGESTED QUESTIONS:

- How many portions of mixed pepper were served on Thursday?
- Which was the least popular salad choice?

Toolkit (page 30)

The speech bubbles illustrate that although the data has been collected, it needs organising and recording in order to make it useful. This activity reinforces the purpose of a frequency table. Model how to set up and complete a frequency table, using data from a different context (for example how children travelled to school, number of siblings). Go round the room and ask children to give the answer to the question.

SUGGESTED QUESTIONS:

- How will you record the number of tools for Year 2?
- How many hand drills does Year 5 have? How will you record this?

Testing times (page 31)

This activity shows grouped data of children's test scores. Discuss how the data has been organised, and check that children understand that each bar shows how many children have scored marks in that group; it is not possible to say from the graph how many children scored, for example, nine marks. Explain that grouped bar charts are used when there would otherwise be very many categories. The extension activity prompts the children to notice the normal distribution of data, although terminology is not required at this stage.

SUGGESTED QUESTIONS:

- Why do you think the data is grouped like this?
- What do you notice about the groupings?

Holiday time: 1 and 2 (pages 32 and 33)

As a whole class, talk about the purpose of grouped data, giving examples of price bands for toys, cars, etc. The data for this activity has been arranged into three price bands: £0–£500, £501–£1000, £1001–£1500. Encourage the children to discuss their ideas for other ways to group the data, letting them discover the problems of price bands that overlap (for example £0–500, £500–£1000…). Access to Internet holiday sites and holiday brochures provides real data for maths activities, including the use of role-play. This data could be revisited for work on different averages.

SUGGESTED QUESTIONS:

- Which is the most expensive holiday?
- If I had £800, how many different holidays could I choose from?
- Which price band does the skiing trip fall into?

Computer scores: 1 and 2 (pages 34 and 35)

The objective of this activity is to group data, thinking about how and why this is done with the emphasis on making the data more manageable. Examples such as grouped scores or ages could be provided to give more global data. Classes in a primary school could be used to show how ages are grouped. Sometimes this might be arbitrary (age cut off at the end of August in UK schools) or at a set level (for example you have to get a certain time or score to get a certain sports award).

SUGGESTED QUESTIONS:

- How is the data grouped?
- Are the groupings the same size?

Strictly statistics: 1 and 2 (pages 36 and 37)

The focus of this activity is on the nature of the data and that a line graph is appropriate because the interim points are meaningful. This could be demonstrated by adding smaller weights to a spring and recording the amount the spring stretches. The children could carry out the practical investigation described, before or after completing the worksheets. Their own data from testing elastic bands/springs could be used instead and plotted on different graphs. The elasticity of the bands/spring will determine the size of weights that should be added.

SUGGESTED QUESTIONS:

- How much did the spring stretch when 600 g were added?
- How can you work out how long the spring would be if 450 g were added?

Spotlight: 1 and 2 (pages 38 and 39)

The data shows the amount of light measured by a light meter. The scale shows 0–5, with 0 as total darkness. The focus is on understanding the shape of the graph and being able to explain what might be happening at different points in the day, rather than interpreting the scale. If there is access to a light meter and related software, this could be set up in an area of the classroom for children to collect data which can be interpreted in a real-life context.

SUGGESTED QUESTIONS:

- When do you think the sun rose?
- What might have happened at 1:00 pm?

Deep blue sea: 1 and 2 (pages 40 and 41)

This activity focuses on choosing appropriate scales for line graphs. Using given data, the children are challenged to think of a meaningful scale. They should be encouraged to justify their choice of scale and then plot the data. The children could carry out further research and draw graphs to accompany this, for example the length of sharks and other fish.

SUGGESTED QUESTIONS:

- What is the length of a blue whale at three years of age?
- How many metres did the dolphin grow in its first year?

Miles to kilometres (page 42)

Using other graphs, such as British pounds to Euros, model how to read off the correct values. Such graphs can be compared to ready reckoners, which some children may find easier to interpret but which do not give interim amounts.

SUGGESTED QUESTIONS:

- How many whole kilometres are there in 5 miles?
- What is the equivalent measurement for 70 kilometres?

You are what you eat (page 43)

This activity introduces the children to pie charts. Warm-up activities could include a focus on division, factors and fractions. Discuss the first pie chart and explain that each mark on the circumference of the circle shows 10°. In this pie chart, the total weight of the ingredients was 360 g, so 10° stands for 10 g. This means that the children can use the chart to give the weight of the different ingredients. Use the second pie chart to show that pie charts can represent different totals. Ask the children to say what fraction of the whole each mark on the circle represents ($\frac{1}{12}$), and ask them to work out one-twelfth of 24. As an extension, the children could list the similarities and differences between the two pie charts.

SUGGESTED QUESTIONS:

- Which weighed more, the sugar or the eggs? How do you know?
- How do you know how many children had crisps?

Hot 'n' tasty: 1 and 2 (pages 44 and 45)

Ensure the children understand that pie charts show proportions of the whole and that charts of the same size do not necessarily have the same total of units represented. Link this activity to division, factors and fractions.

SUGGESTED QUESTIONS:

- Can you explain how you know that five fruity pies were eaten?
- Which pie chart shows the most veggie pies?

Plant sale: 1 and 2 (pages 46 and 47)

This activity requires the children to understand the concept of finding a proportion of a given amount. Each question asks the children to demonstrate a different aspect of their understanding – finding given numbers of plants and finding the total of all plants represented.

SUGGESTED QUESTIONS:

- In which week were the most orchids sold?
- How can you calculate the total number of plants sold?

Per 100 grams (pages 48)

The data taken from a leading brand could be compared with other cereal bars to consider proportions of different nutrients. Although a bar might advertise that it is low in fat, it might be very high in sugar. The children should have access to calculators as they work out percentages for different weight bars.

SUGGESTED QUESTIONS:

- How many grams of fat are there in a bar that weighs 120 g?
- How can you work this out?

Describe and interpret results and solutions to problems using the mode, range, median and mean

The children will be used to finding the mode for a set of data, for example the most popular choice of ice-cream, the most common shoe size. They are now introduced to the other forms of average (the mean, median, and range) as a way of describing a set of data. Ensure the children understand that an average is a number that is used to summarise a set of data. It is useful to discuss with the children how representative they think the different averages are for a particular set of data, and help them to appreciate that one average will usually represent the set of data better than the others.

Home on the range: 1 and 2 (pages 49 and 50)

At the start of the lesson, write two sets of numbers on the board, for example 21, 28, 29, 30, 32, 35 and 11, 45, 63, 72, 81, 112. Ask the children to describe the sets of numbers. Introduce the range as a way to describe whether the pieces of data in a set are close in size or far apart. In the first set of numbers, the range (the difference between the highest and the lowest value) is 14; in the second set the range is 101.

SUGGESTED QUESTIONS:

- What does the 'range' mean?
- How could you calculate this?

Different modes: 1 and 2 (pages 51 and 52)

Discuss the concept of the mode and how the mode could be a value, group of data, colour, etc. The activity shows different representations of data so that the children can see how the mode applies to different scenarios. As a class look at real-life examples, such as ordering stock for a shoe shop to show why different numbers of different-sized shoes are ordered.

SUGGESTED QUESTIONS:

- What does the 'mode' mean?
- What is the mode of this set of data (for example colour of eyes, number of siblings)?

Paul's pool party (page 53)

The sets of data provided are all linked to a swimming pool and require the children to calculate the mean. The data has been planned so that the children should not need a calculator. Encourage the children to think about whether their answer is reasonable. Talk about the mean as the most commonly used 'average'. The last set of data shows how such an average can be meaningless, especially given that a splash pool is not very big! As an extension, ask the children to give the missing value for this set of data with a mean of 8: 6, 13, 9, 3, (9).

SUGGESTED QUESTIONS:

* What is the 'mean' average?
* Is the mean always a number in the set of data? How do you know?

In the middle: 1 and 2 (pages 54 and 55)

Talk about how the median can be useful if there are extreme values that would otherwise skew the mean average. Ensure that the children understand why the data needs to be ordered first.

SUGGESTED QUESTIONS:

* What does the 'median' mean?
* What happens if there is an even number of pieces of data?

Best average (page 56)

By calculating the mean, median and mode for different sets of data, the children are asked to consider which average they think is best for the context given. Discuss how one average could be chosen intentionally to mislead.

SUGGESTED QUESTIONS:

* Which average do you think is the most representative for that data?
* Why would you choose that average?

Side orders (page 57)

Discuss the data given and how the format of the table clearly shows the orders of one side dish across the week and of different dishes for each day. The children may need a calculator to work out the mean averages as decimals are involved.

SUGGESTED QUESTIONS:

* How many orders of chips were there across the week?
* What is the range for the orders of mixed peppers?

Cheeky Chalky (page 58)

Although the concepts of range and average are not new, the children are now required to find the missing value using the given average. As a whole class, talk about what strategies would be helpful to calculate the missing value.

SUGGESTED QUESTIONS:

* What do you need to do to find out the median?
* How do you know that that is the missing value?
* Is there anything that you could do to check?

Cube collection (page 59)

Talk about why giving everyone three attempts and then finding the average score is often used to reduce effects of first attempts and practice. The children will have to justify their choice of average, given that everyone is going to want to use the one that shows their score as the best.

SUGGESTED QUESTIONS:

* How will you measure how many cubes are picked up?
* Why do you think that average is the fairest one to use?

Beijing 2008 (page 60)

The data shows the results from the Olympic Games for 2008. Websites and other resources for the Games give a wealth of data for different sports, many of which the children may have seen. The data presented in the table gives fractions of a second. Talk about how the lowest number in a race is the best result.

SUGGESTED QUESTIONS:

* How many athletes were faster than 10 seconds?
* What was the difference in time between the runner who came first and the runner who came last?

Resources

This section contains a blank line graph and blank spinners for the children to use. The graph can be used in several ways: on the interactive whiteboard for whole-class activities, or copied for individuals or pairs to complete. It can be used: with data prepared by the teacher or by individuals or small groups, blank for children to collect and present data, to support activities in this book, as part of extension activities where children present the data from a worksheet in a different format.

Blank line graph (page 61)

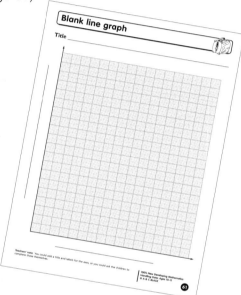

Blank spinners (page 62)

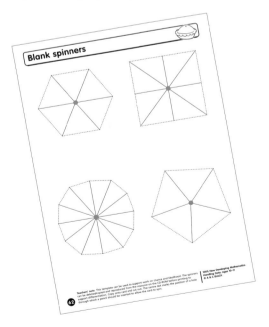

Using the CD-ROM

The PC CD-ROM included with this book contains an easy-to-use software program that allows you to print out pages from the book, to view them (e.g. on an interactive whiteboard) or to customise the activities to suit the needs of your pupils.

Getting started
It's easy to run the software. Simply insert the CD-ROM into your CD drive and the disk should autorun and launch the interface in your web browser.

If the disk does not autorun, open 'My Computer' and select the CD drive, then open the file 'start.html'.

Please note: this CD-ROM is designed for use on a PC. It will also run on most Apple Macintosh computers in Safari however, due to the differences between Mac and PC fonts, you may experience some unavoidable variations in the typography and page layouts of the activity sheets.

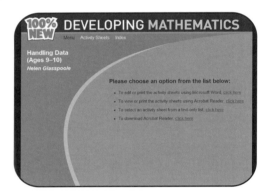

The Menu screen
Four options are available to you from the main menu screen.

The first option takes you to the Activity Sheets screen, where you can choose an activity sheet to edit or print out using Microsoft Word.

(If you do not have the Microsoft Office suite, you might like to consider using OpenOffice instead. This is a multi-platform and multi-lingual office suite, and an 'open-source' project. It is compatible with all other major office suites, and the product is free to download, use and distribute. The homepage for OpenOffice on the Internet is: www.openoffice.org.)

The second option on the main menu screen opens a PDF file of the entire book using Adobe Reader (see below). This format is ideal for printing out copies of the activity sheets or for displaying them, for example on an interactive whiteboard.

The third option allows you to choose a page to edit from a text-only list of the activity sheets, as an alternative to the graphical interface on the Activity Sheets screen.

Adobe Reader is free to download and to use. If it is not already installed on your computer, the fourth link takes you to the download page on the Adobe website.

You can also navigate directly to any of the three screens at any time by using the tabs at the top.

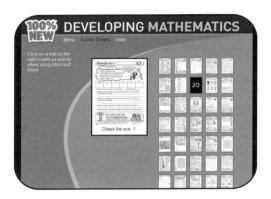

The Activity Sheets screen
This screen shows thumbnails of all the activity sheets in the book. Rolling the mouse over a thumbnail highlights the page number and also brings up a preview image of the page.

Click on the thumbnail to open a version of the page in Microsoft Word (or an equivalent software program, see above.) The full range of editing tools are available to you here to customise the page to suit the needs of your particular pupils. You can print out copies of the page or save a copy of your edited version onto your computer.

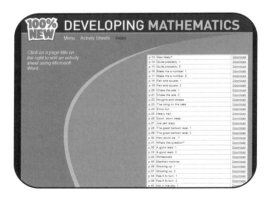

The Index screen
This is a text-only version of the Activity Sheets screen described above. Choose an activity sheet and click on the 'download' link to open a version of the page in Microsoft Word to edit or print out.

Technical support
If you have any questions regarding the *100% New Developing Literacy* or *Developing Mathematics* software, please email us at the address below. We will get back to you as quickly as possible.

educationalsales@acblack.com

Ferry times: 1

Mr Perry, the ferryman, tries hard
to keep to his timetable.

You need Ferry times: 2.

- **Look at the timetable on Ferry times: 2.**
- **What is the likelihood of a ferry leaving the jetty at the following times?**

Write the letter in the correct section of the table.

A Tuesday	**B** 17:20 on a Thursday
C 22:00 on a Bank holiday	**D** 08:15 on a Saturday
E 11:15 on a Monday	**F** 20:25 on a Sunday
G 04:00 on a weekday	**H** 23:30 on a Friday

Impossible	Very unlikely	Unlikely	Very likely	Certain
				A

NOW TRY THIS!

- **Complete this statement.**

  It is very likely that a ferry will leave the jetty
  at _____ on a _____.

Teachers' note Use in conjunction with page 14, Ferry times: 2. Check that the children can interpret the timetable on page 14, in particular what is meant by 'then every…', and that they understand the 24-hour clock times. At the start of the lesson, revise the vocabulary of likelihood, asking for examples of events that can be described as 'certain' or 'impossible'.

100% New Developing Mathematics
Handling Data: Ages 10–11
© A & C BLACK

Ferry times from this jetty

Monday – Thursday	Friday	Saturday	Sunday
06:30	06:30	06:30	07:00
07:00	07:00	07:00	Then every half an hour until
07:30	07:30	07:30	09:00
Then every quarter of an hour until 09:00	Then every quarter of an hour until 09:00	Then every quarter of an hour until 09:00	Then every hour until 22:00
Then every half an hour until 17:00	Then every half an hour until 17:00	Then every half an hour until 17:00	**Bank holidays**
17:15	17:15	17:15	09:00
17:30	17:30	17:30	Then every hour until 21:00
17:45	17:45	17:45	
18:00	18:00	18:00	
Then every hour until 22:00	Then every half an hour until 00:00	Then every half an hour until 00:00	

Teachers' note Use in conjunction with page 13, Ferry times: 1.

14

100% New Developing Mathematic
Handling Data: Ages 10–11
© A & C BLACK

Chess guess: 1

You need Chess guess: 2.

There are 32 pieces in a chess set.
Sam puts all the pieces into a cloth bag
and picks one out without looking.

1 Which of the following chess pieces is she **more likely** to pick?

Underline the piece that you think I am **more likely** to pick.
If you think it is **equally likely**, underline both pieces.

a a knight or a queen?

c a pawn or a black piece?

e a knight or a rook?

b a rook or a white piece?

d a black piece or a bishop?

f a white king or a black rook?

2 Complete these statements.

    a Sam is less likely to pick a _____ than a _____.

    b Sam is more likely to pick a _____ than a _____.

    c Sam is equally likely to pick a _____ as a _____.

3 a Which type of chess piece is she **most likely** to pick? _____

    b Why do you think so? _____

_____

**NOW TRY
THIS!**

Sam is more likely to pick
a queen than a king.

That's wrong!

• **Talk to a partner about who you think is right
and explain your reasoning.**

Teachers' note Use in conjunction with page 16, Chess guess: 2. No prior knowledge of chess is needed, though it would be useful to have available a chess set so that the children can see and discuss the data for this activity. (Note: some children might know a 'rook' as a 'castle'.) The children can use the chess pieces as data for other questions and statements to discuss in pairs.

*100% New Developing Mathematics
Handling Data: Ages 10–11
© A & C BLACK*

Chess guess: 2

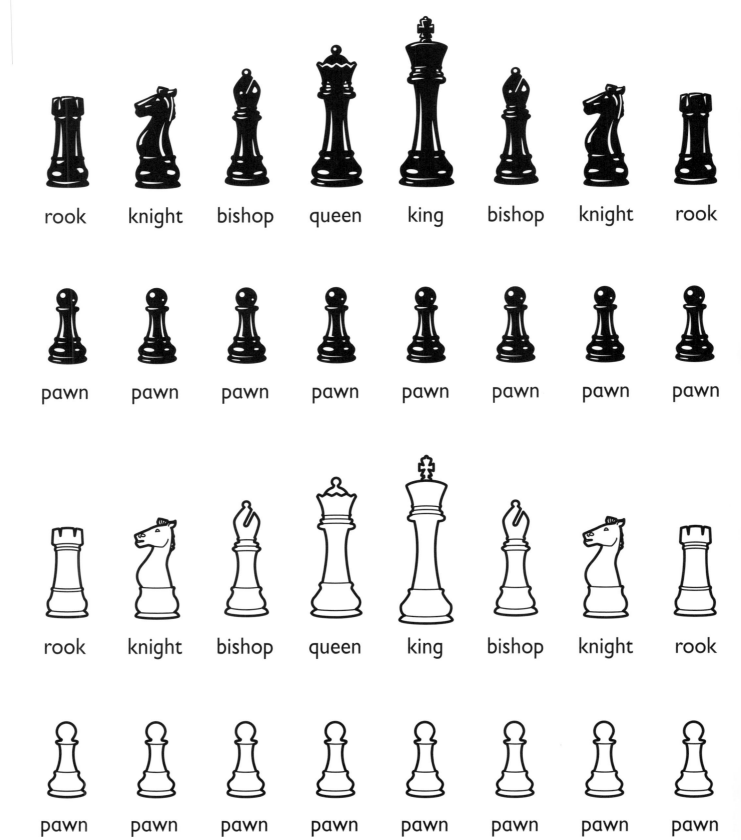

| rook | knight | bishop | queen | king | bishop | knight | rook |

| pawn | pawn | pawn | pawn | pawn | pawn | pawn | pawn |

| rook | knight | bishop | queen | king | bishop | knight | rook |

| pawn | pawn | pawn | pawn | pawn | pawn | pawn | pawn |

Teachers' note Use in conjunction with page 15, Chess guess: 1.

100% New Developing Mathema
Handling Data: Ages 10–11
© A & C BLACK

Chance landing

A

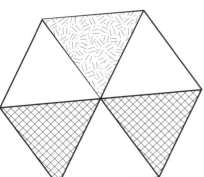

B

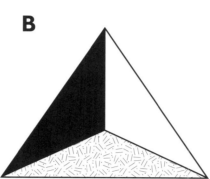

C

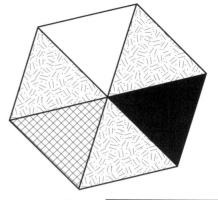

D

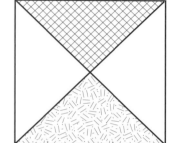

1 Which spinner is most likely to land on ⊠ ? ____

2 Which spinner is least likely to land on ▨ ? ____

3 Tick **true** or **false** for each statement.

    a C is more likely to land on ⊠ than on ☐ .   True ☐   False ☐

    b D is more likely to land on ▨ than on ⊠ .   True ☐   False ☐

    c B is more likely to land on ▨ than on ■ .   True ☐   False ☐

4 How likely is it that each spinner will land on ☐ ?

    Choose from: impossible, unlikely, a fifty-fifty chance, likely, certain.

    A _____   B _____

    C _____   D _____

5 Complete the statements.

    Choose from: impossible, unlikely, a fifty-fifty chance, likely, certain.

    It is ___*unlikely*___ that spinner _A_ will land on ▨ .

    It is _____ that spinner ___ will land on ■ .

    It is _____ that spinner ___ will land on ≋ .

NOW TRY THIS!

- **Which is more likely: that spinner C will land on** **or that spinner D will land on ☐ ?**
- **Explain your thinking to a partner.**

Teachers' note This activity should be completed before page 18, Shady business. The children could use page 62, Blank spinners, to experiment with their own shading and colouring. From this they could write their own statements and challenge others with questions about the spinners.

100% New Developing Mathematics
Handling Data: Ages 10–11
© A & C BLACK

Shady business

- **Follow the instructions for each spinner.**

A

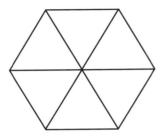

Shade the spinner so that it is **more likely** to land on ▉ than on ▨.

B

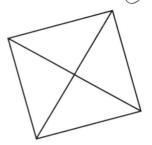

Shade the spinner so that it is **less likely** to land on ☐ than on ▨.

C

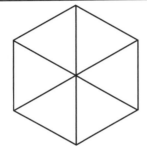

Shade the spinner so that it is **certain** to land on ▨.

D

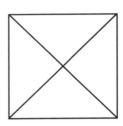

Colour the spinner so that it is **equally likely** to land on green as on red.

E

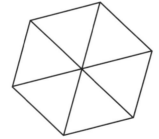

Colour the spinner so that it is **impossible** to land on red.

F

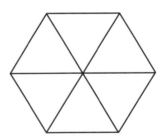

Colour the spinner so that it is **very likely** to land on blue.

G

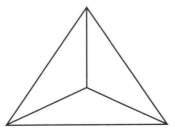

Colour the spinner so that it is **more likely** to land on green than on blue.

H

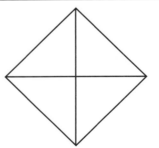

Colour the spinner so that it is **impossible** to land on green or white.

Teachers' note This activity develops concepts introduced on page 17, Chance landing. The children could use page 62, Blank spinners, to set or respond to challenges linked to chance and probability, for example they could write their own statements and challenge others with questions about the spinners. Colouring pencils are required for this activity.

100% New Developing Mathema **Handling Data: Ages 10–11** © A & C BLACK

A dice landing on 6 	A coin landing on 'heads' or 'tails' 	A dice landing on an even number 
Picking 'September' from a pack of 'months of the year' cards 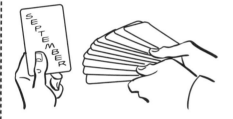	Picking a white piece from a chess set 	A dice landing on 3 
Throwing a total of 12 with two dice 	Throwing a total of 7 with two dice 	A coin landing on 'heads' 
Picking a pawn from a chess set 	This spinner landing on the shaded part 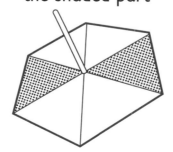	Picking a black piece from a chess set 

Teachers' note Use in conjunction with page 20, More likely: 2. The children play the game in pairs or small groups. Each pair/group will need one set of cards. (See page 6 for instructions on how to play the game.) The statements on the cards relate to something being picked at random from a whole set. Individuals or pairs could also order events from least likely to most likely.

100% New Developing Mathematics
Handling Data: Ages 10–11
© A & C BLACK

A coin landing on 'tails'

Picking a vowel from a pack of alphabet cards

A dice landing on an odd number

Picking a 7 from a pack of 0–9 digit cards

Picking a white king from a chess set

Picking a circle from these shapes

Picking a square from these shapes.

Throwing two dice and one landing on 3

Picking 'Tuesday' from a pack of 'days of the week' cards

This spinner landing on the shaded part

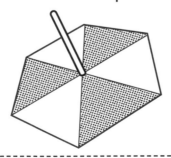

This spinner landing on the shaded part

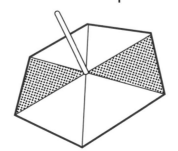

This spinner landing on the shaded part

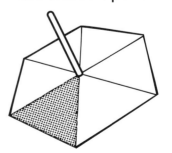

Teachers' note Use in conjunction with page 19, More likely: 1. No prior knowledge of chess is needed, though it would be useful to have available a chess set so that the children can see and discuss the data for this activity.

100% New Developing Mathem **Handling Data: Ages 10–11** © A & C BLACK

Finding out

- **With a partner, discuss how you could find the answers to the problems below.**

A How much water does our class use in one week?

B On average, which class at our school has the most amount of sleep per week?

C How many children attend our school? Is this different from the number when our school first opened?

D How many kilometres do I walk during a typical week?

- **Which is the easiest investigation to carry out?** ____
- **Why do you think so?** _____

_____

- **Which investigation is the most difficult to collect data for?** ____
- **Why do you think so?** _____

_____

- **Choose the investigation that you are most interested in.** ____
- **What data would you need to collect? How could you collect it?**

_____

_____

_____

Teachers' note If appropriate, the children could suggest their own lines of enquiry to investigate. Encourage them to think about whether the problems need refining and how to ensure accurate data collection.

100% New Developing Mathematics
Handling Data: Ages 10–11
© A & C BLACK

Weather station

- **What data could you collect about the weather?**
- **Talk to a partner about some investigations you could carry out and record your ideas below.**

- **Choose one investigation.**
- **How will you collect and record the data?**

_____

_____

_____

_____

> **Think!**
> Will you be able to collect the data all in one go? Or will you have to take measurements every day for a week, or every hour in a day?

- **On paper or using ICT, design a recording sheet.**
- **What do you predict the data will tell you?** _____

_____

_____

Teachers' note Discuss ideas about how to collect data. If possible, make simple recording instruments to measure rainfall. The children will need plain, squared or lined paper for their recording sheets. Alternatively, these could be designed using ICT and presented on an interactive whiteboard for discussion and evaluation.

100% New Developing Mathema
Handling Data: Ages 10–11
© A & C BLACK

In conclusion: 1

You need the worksheets called In conclusion: 2, 3 and 4.

Work with a partner.

- **Use the charts and graphs to help you answer the questions on each worksheet.**

Bar chart to show the number of goals scored each week in the Under 12 girls' and boys' football league

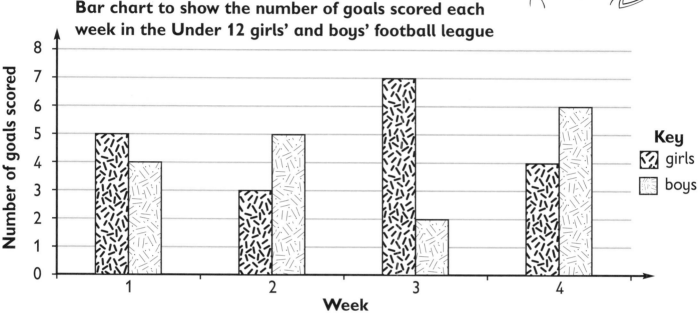

Key
girls
boys

1 How many goals did the girls score in week 2? _____

2 How many goals did the boys score altogether? _____

Girls are better at football than boys.

3 a Based on the results, do you think that this statement is true? _____

  b Explain your answer. _____

  _____

  _____

  c What further data could you collect to check your answer?

  _____

  _____

Teachers' note Use in conjunction with pages 24, 25 and 26, In conclusion: 2, 3 and 4. Discuss the term 'in conclusion' and the limitations of data. What does/doesn't the data tell you? What conclusions can be drawn? What further information should be gathered? Should we use experience to inform ideas, even if the data suggests otherwise?

100% New Developing Mathematics Handling Data: Ages 10–11 © A & C BLACK

In conclusion: 2

A school carried out a sponsored sports challenge.
They raised £288.

Pie chart to show the money raised by each class

Key
☐ Class 1
▧ Class 2
▨ Class 3
▥ Class 4
■ Class 5
▦ Class 6

1 Which classes each raised £24? _____

2 How much money did Class 3 raise? _____

3 'Class 4 is the best at sport.' What do you think about this statement?
Record your ideas below.

4 a 'Class 4 care the most about charity.'
Do you think the results show this statement to be true? _____

b Why do you think Class 4 raised the most money? _____
_____
_____

Teachers' note Use in conjunction with pages 23, 25 and 26, In conclusion: 1, 3 and 4. Discuss the pie chart and how it shows data. Check the children understand that the larger the fraction that is shaded, the more money was raised. Ask them to say roughly what fraction of the £288 was raised by each class, and ask for suggestions as to how to work out how much this is.

100% New Developing Mathema
Handling Data: Ages 10–11
© A & C BLACK

You need the worksheet called In conclusion: 4.

● **Look at the line graphs and bar charts.**

1 In which months was it hottest in London?

_____

2 What was the lowest temperature recorded in Rome? _____ °C

3 In which month was there 50 mm of rain in London? _____

4 How much rain fell in Rome in January? _____ mm

5 a 'Rome gets more rain than London'.
   Based on the results, do you think this statement is true? _____

b Explain your answer. _____

_____

_____

6 a 'The hotter it is, the dryer it is.' Do you agree with this? _____

b Is this true for London and Rome? _____

c Explain your answer. _____

_____

_____

7 On the back of this sheet, write two questions about the data for a partner to answer.

It is difficult to draw conclusions from some sets of data.

● **Do you agree with this statement?** _____
● **Talk to a partner about your ideas.**

Teachers' note Use in conjunction with pages 23, 24 and 26, In conclusion: 1, 2 amd 4.

100% New Developing Mathematics
Handling Data: Ages 10–11
© A & C BLACK

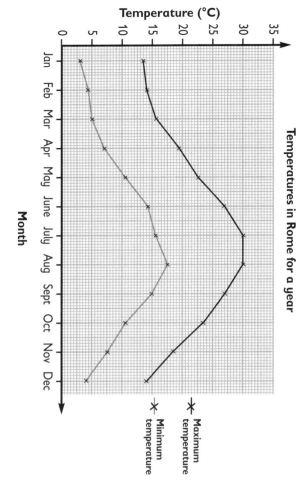

Temperatures in Rome for a year

Temperature (°C)

Month

Minimum temperature

Maximum temperature

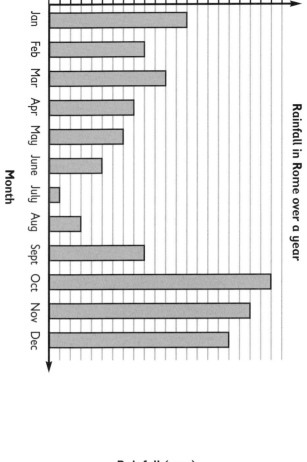

Rainfall in Rome over a year

Rainfall (mm)

Month

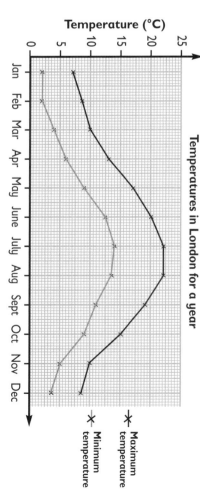

Temperatures in London for a year

Temperature (°C)

Month

Minimum temperature

Maximum temperature

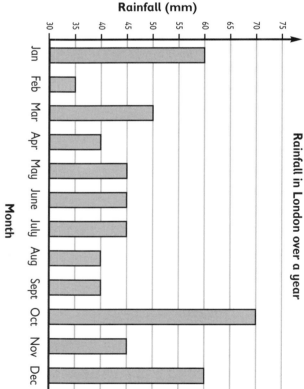

Rainfall in London over a year

Rainfall (mm)

Month

Teachers' note Use in conjunction with pages 23, 24 and 25, In conclusion: 1, 2 and 3.

100% New Developing Mathem
Handling Data: Ages 10–11
© A & C BLACK

Mike's and Spike's bikes: 1

The frequency table shows the number of bikes sold at Mike's and Spike's bike shops last year.

	Jan	Feb	Mar	Apr	May	June	July	Aug	Sept	Oct	Nov	Dec
Mike	58	21	28	35	48	61	68	73	47	36	18	49
Spike	65	17	0	0	53	55	61	64	37	27	14	35

1 Who sold the most bikes in June? _____

2 Mike sold 58 bikes in the January sale.

  a Was this more or fewer than Spike? _____

  b What was the difference in the number sold? ___

3 Why do you think that the number of sales was so low in November and February? _____

_____

4 How could you explain the number of sales in Spike's shop for March and April? _____

_____

5 a Who sold the most bikes during the year? _____

  b How many bikes were sold by both shops in total? _____

Use a calculator to help you.

NOW TRY THIS!

• **In which month was there the greatest difference in the number of sales between Mike's and Spike's shops?** _____

Teachers' note Use in conjunction with page 28, Mike's and Spike's bikes: 2. Calculators should be made available to support calculation for the final question.

100% New Developing Mathematics
Handling Data: Ages 10–11
© A & C BLACK

Mike's and Spike's bikes: 2

The frequency table shows the number of bike lights sold at Mike's and Spike's bike shops.

	Jan	Feb	Mar	Apr	May	June	July	Aug	Sept	Oct	Nov	Dec
Mike	14	26	28	17	8	7	8	12	45	51	38	20
Spike	9	18	0	0	6	6	3	5	15	19	21	44

1 a Who do you think had a Christmas offer on bike lights? _____

  b Why do you think this? _____

_____

2 In total, how many bike lights were sold in August? _____

3 a Who sold the most bike lights overall? _____

  b How many lights were sold in total? _____

4 Why do you think that more lights were sold in some parts of the year than in others? Try to explain the results and draw some conclusions.

Use a calculator to help you.

_____

_____

_____

_____

_____

_____

_____

Teachers' note Use in conjunction with page 27, Mike's and Spike's bikes: 1. Calculators should be made available to support calculation for question 3.

100% New Developing Mathemat
Handling Data: Ages 10–11
© A & C BLACK

Salad bar

The number of salad portions served in a café was recorded for one week.

		Monday	Tuesday	Wednesday	Thursday	Friday	Frequency for week
Grated carrot		卌 卌 ‖	卌 ‖‖	卌 卌 ‖‖	卌 卌 ‖‖‖	卌 卌	57
Sweetcorn		卌 ‖	‖‖‖	‖‖‖	卌	卌 ‖	
Lettuce		卌 ‖‖‖	卌 卌 ‖	卌 ‖‖‖	卌 ‖‖	卌 卌	
Beetroot		卌 ‖‖	卌 ‖	卌 卌 ‖	卌 卌 ‖	卌 卌 ‖	
Mixed pepper		卌 卌 ‖‖‖	卌 卌 卌	卌 卌 ‖	卌 卌 ‖‖	卌 卌 ‖‖	
Cucumber		卌 卌 ‖‖‖	卌 ‖‖‖	卌 卌	卌 卌	卌 ‖‖‖	

- **Complete the frequency table and answer these questions.**

1 What was the most popular salad choice overall? _____

2 How many portions of beetroot were served in total? _____

3 What was the **least** popular choice on Monday? _____

4 On which day were 12 portions of lettuce served? _____

5 Five portions of a salad choice were served on one day.
   a What was the salad choice? _____
   b On which day was it served? _____

6 Who do you think this data is useful for?

Discuss your ideas with a partner.

NOW TRY THIS!

60 portions of salad were served on Friday.

- **Do you agree with this statement?** _____
- **Explain your answer to your partner.**

Teachers' note Discuss the layout of the frequency chart to ensure that the children understand what each cell represents. As a further extension, the children could draw bar charts to represent the data.

100% New Developing Mathematics
Handling Data: Ages 10–11
© A & C BLACK

Toolkit

Class 6W investigated how many different tools each class in their school had.

Year 5 have 12 hammers, 5 glue guns, 8 hand drills and 10 saws.

Year 1 have 10 saws and 6 hammers.

Year 3 have 15 hammers and 4 hand drills.

Year 2 use the tools from Year 1 as there's no room to store them in the classroom.

Reception have no tools.

Year 4 share with year 3.

Year 6 have 11 hand drills, 7 glue guns, 10 saws and 4 hammers.

- **Organise the data into a frequency table.**
- **Write headings for the table.**

- **On the back of this sheet, write two statements about the data.**

NOW TRY THIS!

- **The head teacher wants to make sure that there are at least fifteen of each tool in school.**
- **Write the number of tools she needs to order.**

saws ☐   glue guns ☐   hammers ☐   hand drills ☐

Teachers' note Discuss the purpose of a frequency table and how it could be set up before data collection to facilitate clear recording. Using other data, such as number of pens/pencils in pencil cases, revise how a tally system works.

100% New Developing Mathemat
Handling Data: Ages 10–11
© A & C BLACK

Testing times

Maisy's class took a test. There were 14 marks in total. The bar chart shows the children's scores.

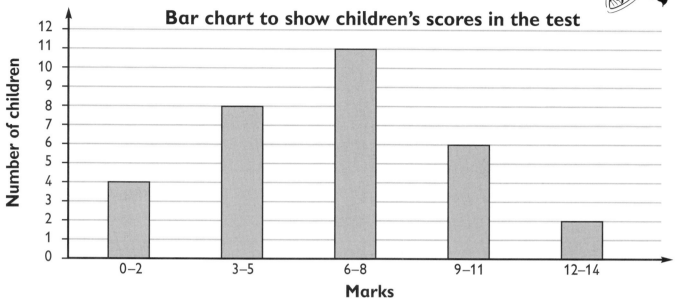

Bar chart to show children's scores in the test

(Y-axis: Number of children, 0 to 12)
(X-axis: Marks — 0–2, 3–5, 6–8, 9–11, 12–14)

- **Use the bar chart to answer these questions.**

1 How many children scored two marks or less? _____

2 How many children scored nine marks or more? _____

3 How many children were in the class altogether? _____

4 Does the data tell you Maisy's score in the test? _____

5 Do you think the data could be presented in another way?

Discuss your ideas with a partner.

NOW TRY THIS!

- **What do you notice about the shape of the bar chart?**

Talk to your partner about your ideas.

Teachers' note This activity focuses on the purpose of grouping data and helps the children to understand the strengths and limitations of doing this.

100% New Developing Mathematics
Handling Data: Ages 10–11
© A & C BLACK

Holiday time: 1

A holiday company offers holidays at set prices.

Holiday package	Price per person (£)
Nile cruise	675
Greek island tour	395
'Down under' expedition round Australia	1080
Skiing in the Alps	550
Experience India	940
Luxury safari in East Africa	1500
Mexican dreams	750
Brazil and beyond	625
Sailing in Croatia	450
European city break tour: Paris — Florence — Madrid	320
South African safari, summits and surf	800
Moroccan mini-break	295
Iceland — ice and fire	925

- **Use tallying to show how many holidays are in each price band.**

Cheapest Price band: £0–£500	Medium Price band: £501–£1000	Most expensive Price band: £1001–£1500

- **Represent this** grouped data **on a bar chart by showing how many holidays are in each price band.**

Use the bar chart on holiday time: 2.

NOW TRY THIS!

- **What is the** range **of holiday prices shown in the chart?**

Teachers' note Use in conjunction with page 33, Holiday time: 2. Discuss the concept of price bands and the significance of equal price bands. Further extension work could include data from holiday internet sites and travel brochures. Data could also be used to discuss the range, mean, median and mode.

100% New Developing Mathema*
Handling Data: Ages 10–11
© A & C BLACK

Holiday time: 2

Bar chart to show the number of holidays in each price band

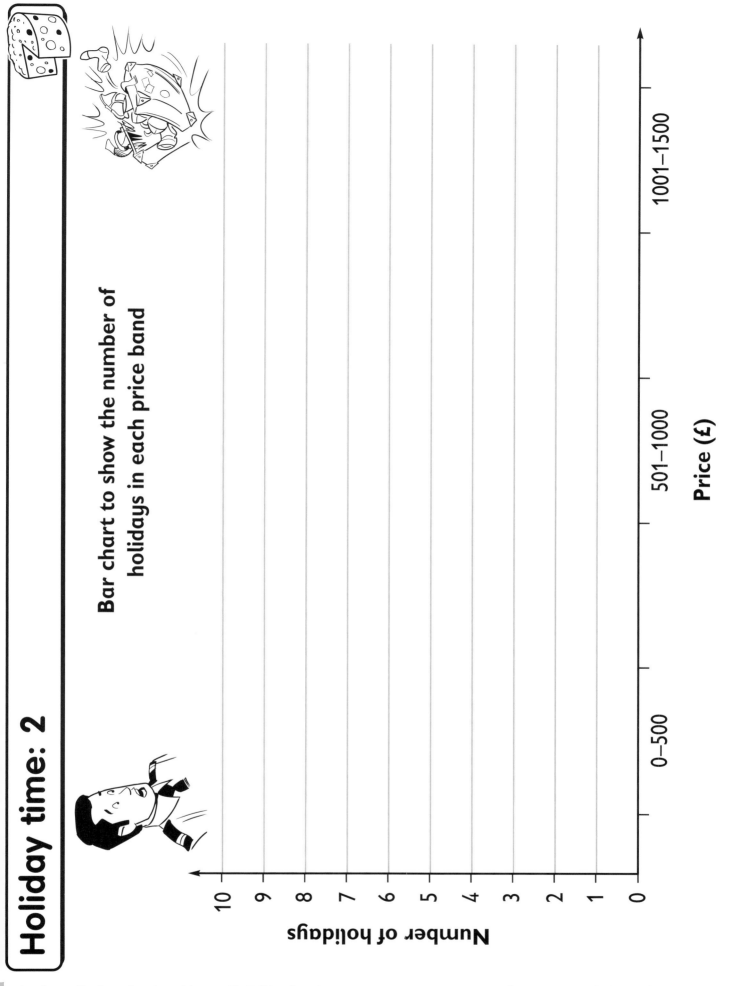

Number of holidays

10
9
8
7
6
5
4
3
2
1
0

Price (£)

0–500   501–1000   1001–1500

100% New Developing Mathematics
Handling Data: Ages 10–11
© A & C BLACK

33

Computer scores: 1

Here are some computer game scores.

Amy 120
Billy 55
Meena 1600
Freya 1200
Ella 750
Ruby 1950
Alfie 420
Harry 900
Ajit 110
Terri 1700

• **Write each name in the correct column of the table.**

0–400 points	401–800 points	801–1200 points	1201–1600 points	1601–2000 points
Amy				

• **Represent this grouped data on a bar chart.**

Use the bar chart on Computer scores: 2.

NOW TRY THIS!

• **Kelvin's score is in the same group as Freya's.**
• **What could his lowest and highest scores be?**

lowest score _____   highest score _____

Teachers' note Use in conjunction with page 35, Computer scores: 2. Discuss scenarios where grouping data is useful.

100% New Developing Mathema
Handling Data: Ages 10–11
© A & C BLACK

Computer scores: 2

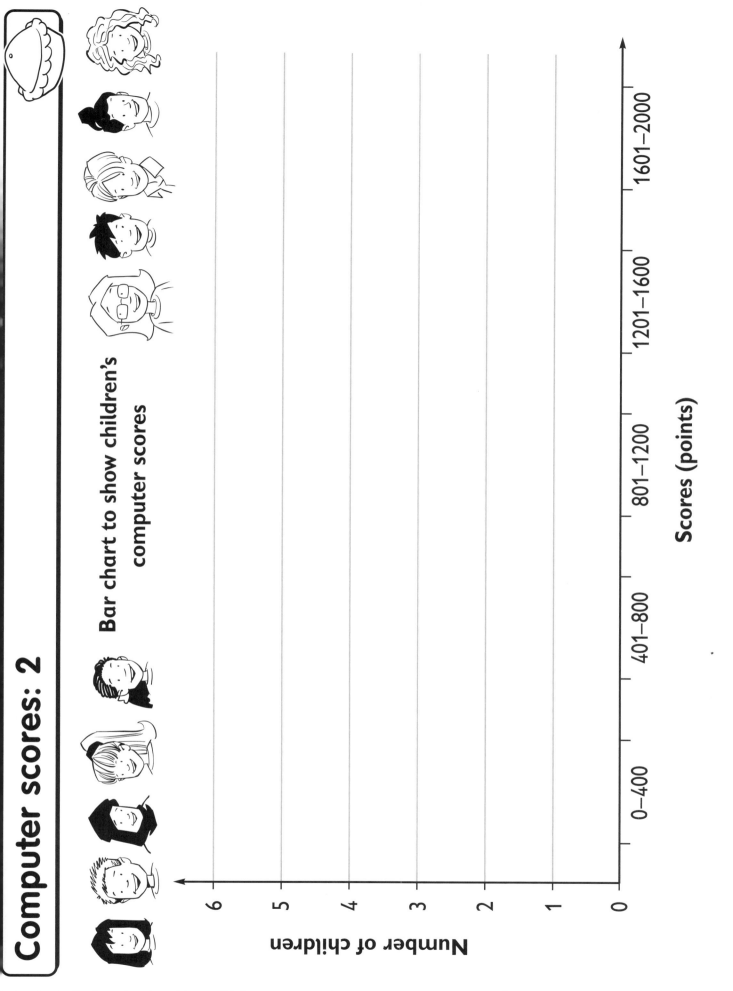

Bar chart to show children's computer scores

Number of children

6
5
4
3
2
1
0

0–400 401–800 801–1200 1201–1600 1601–2000

Scores (points)

Teachers' note Use in conjunction with page 34, Computer scores: 1.

100% New Developing Mathematics
Handling Data: Ages 10–11
© A & C BLACK

Stretchy statistics: 1

Class 6S measured how far three springs stretched when different weights were added. Here are the results for Spring B.

Weight added	0 g	100 g	200 g	300 g	400 g	500 g	600 g	700 g	800 g
Length of spring	8·5 cm	9 cm	9·5 cm	10 cm	10·5 cm	11 cm	11·5 cm	12 cm	12·5 cm

- **Plot the data for Spring B as a line graph.**

Use the line graph on Stretchy statistics: 2.

1 What was the length of spring B before any weights were added? _____ cm

2 How many centimetres long was spring B when 800 g were added? _____ cm

3 What would be the approximate length of spring B when 250 g were added? _____ cm

NOW TRY THIS!

- **Which spring stretched the furthest?** ___

Weight added	Length of spring		
	A	**B**	**C**
0 g	8 cm	8·5 cm	9 cm
800 g	10 cm	12·5 cm	12·5 cm

Teachers' note Use in conjunction with page 37, Stretchy statistics: 2. This activity could be linked to the class carrying out the investigation in a science lesson. Data generated from weights added to elastic bands or springs could be plotted, compared and discussed. Simple conclusions could be made and further lines of enquiry suggested.

100% New Developing Mathem[e]
Handling Data: Ages 10–11
© A & C BLACK

Line graph to show the length of spring B

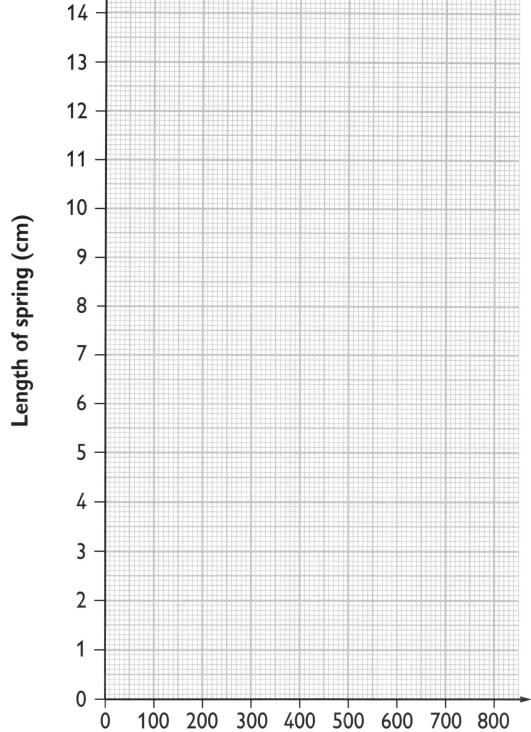

Teachers' note Use in conjunction with page 36, Stretchy statistics: 1.

100% New Developing Mathematics
Handling Data: Ages 10–11
© A & C BLACK

Spotlight: 1

These children set up a light meter to measure how much light entered their classroom during one day.

They drew a line graph of their results. You will find it on the worksheet called Spot light: 2.

- **Look at the line graph and answer these questions.**

1 At what time did the sun start to rise? _____

2 What do you think happened between 3:00 pm and 8:00 pm? _____

_____

3 The curtains were partly closed during the day. When was this?_____

4 What do you think happened at 10:00 pm?

_____

_____

5 a What time of year do you think it is? _____

b Why do you think this? _____

_____

6 On the back of this sheet, write three more questions about the data for a partner to solve.

NOW TRY THIS!

- **For how many hours was the room in total darkness? ____ hours**

Teachers' note Use in conjunction with page 39, Spotlight: 2. If there is access to a light meter, it could be set up in a part of the classroom for 24 hours and the data used to construct/interpret line graphs. The children could discuss the data above in pairs, before looking at the questions.

100% New Developing Mathema
Handling Data: Ages 10–11
© A & C BLACK

Spotlight: 2

Line graph to show the amount of light that entered a room during a day

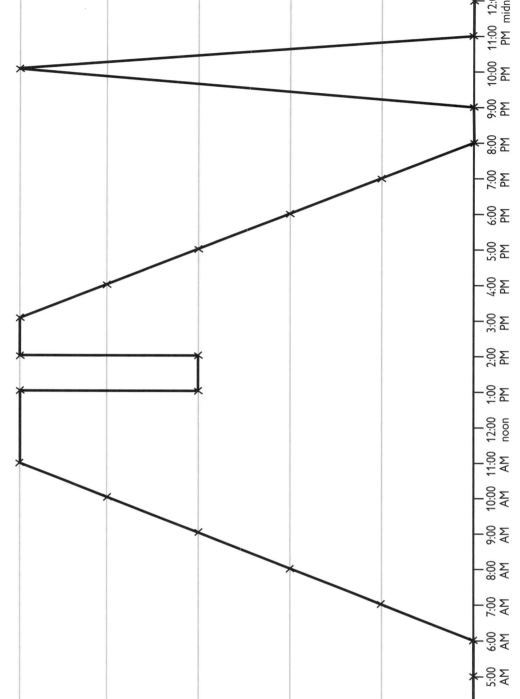

Amount of light detected

Time of day

100% New Developing Mathematics
Handling Data: Ages 10–11
© **A & C BLACK**

39

Deep blue sea: 1

Length of a female bottlenose dolphin

Age	Birth	1 year	2 years	3 years	4 years	5 years
Length	0·8 m	1·4 m	1·7 m	2 m	2·3 m	2·5 m

Length of a female blue whale

Age	Birth	1 year	2 years	3 years	4 years	5 years
Length	7 m	18 m	21 m	22 m	23 m	24 m

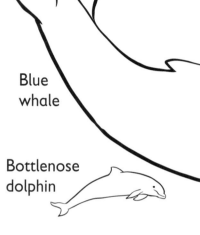

Blue whale

Bottlenose dolphin

- **Plot the data in the tables onto two line graphs.**

Use the line graphs on Deep blue sea: 2.

1 How did you decide what scale to use? _____

_____

2 Did you use the same scale as your partner? _____

- **Use your line graphs to answer these questions.**

3 Approximately how long is a female bottlenose dolphin at $3\frac{1}{2}$ years of age? _____ m

Did you know?
The longest blue whale ever recorded was 31 m. This is longer than a netball court!

4 Approximately how old is a female blue whale when she is 20 m in length? ____ years ____ months

NOW TRY THIS!

- **From birth to 5 years of age, how much did each creature grow?**

  a Bottlenose dolphin _____ m   **b** Blue whale _____ m

Teachers' note Use in conjunction with page 41, Deep blue sea: 2. Discuss the different scales used for different graphs and whether the scale on the y-axis needs to start at zero. The children could talk in pairs about an appropriate scale before plotting the data on the graphs. When answering question 4, discuss how to work out the age in years and months.

100% New Developing Mathema
Handling Data: Ages 10–11
© A & C BLACK

Deep blue sea: 2

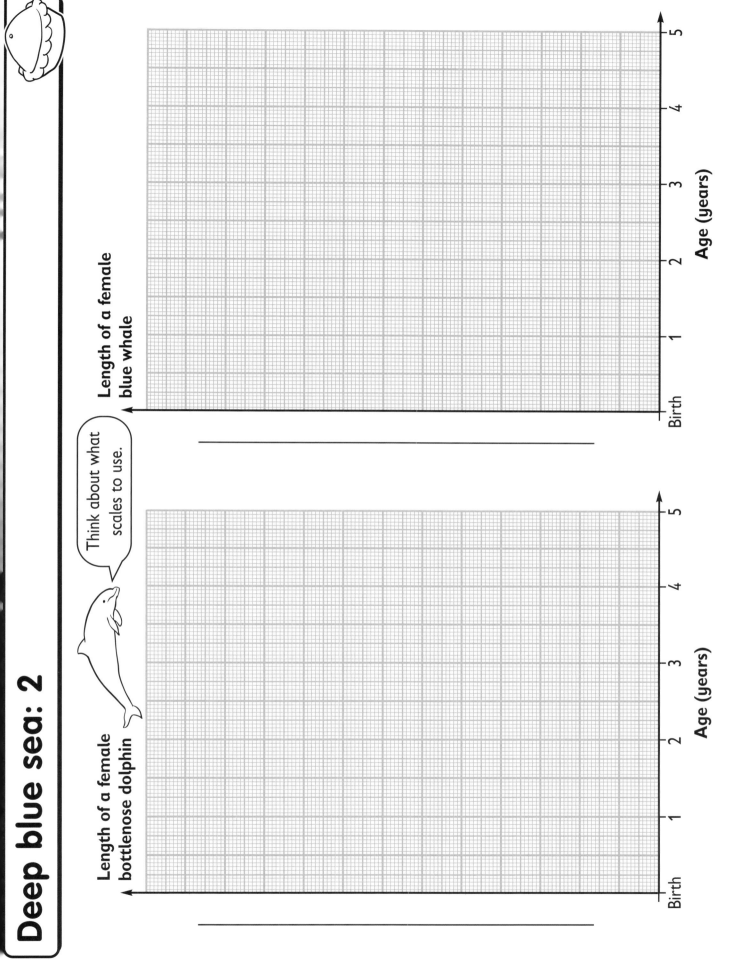

Length of a female
bottlenose dolphin

Think about what
scales to use.

Age (years)

Length of a female
blue whale

Age (years)

Teachers' note Use in conjunction with page 40, Deep blue sea: 1.

100% New Developing Mathematics
Handling Data: Ages 10–11
© A & C BLACK

Miles to kilometres

• **Milly drew a** $\boxed{\text{conversion graph}}$ **for miles and kilometres.**

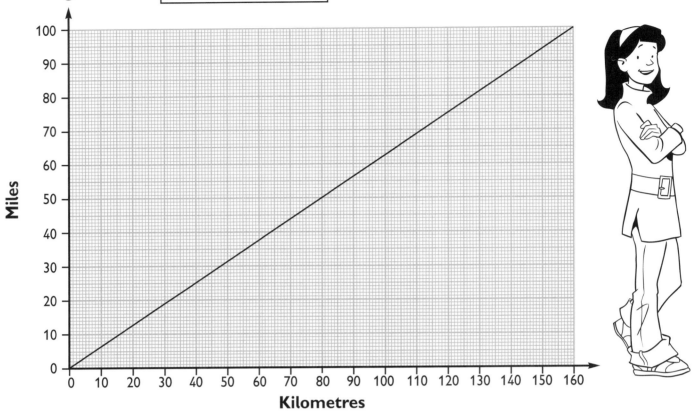

• **Use the graph to complete these statements.**

1 a 50 miles = _____ km

b 100 miles = _____ km

c 10 miles = _____ km

d 62 miles = _____ km

e 35 miles = _____ km

2 a 40 km = _____ miles

b 120 km = _____ miles

c 95 km = _____ miles

d 5 km = _____ miles

e 150 km = _____ miles

• **Use the statements above to work out these conversions.**

3 a 1 mile = _____ km

b 1 km = _____ miles

NOW TRY THIS!

• **On the back of this sheet, explain how knowing that 100 miles = 160 km can help you to calculate what 2 miles is equivalent to.**

Teachers' note Talk about why the graph is a straight line and explain that the values are approximations only. Discuss the use of conversion graphs for other contexts, such as money and temperature.

100% New Developing Mathema **Handling Data: Ages 10–11** © A & C BLACK

You are what you eat

- **Answer the questions about the pie charts.**

1 How many different cake ingredients were used? _____

2 Which ingredient was:
  a the heaviest? _____
  b the lightest? _____

3 The total weight of the ingredients was 360 g. What was the weight of each ingredient?

  a margarine _____ g
  b sugar _____ g
  c fruit _____ g
  d eggs _____ g
  e flour _____ g

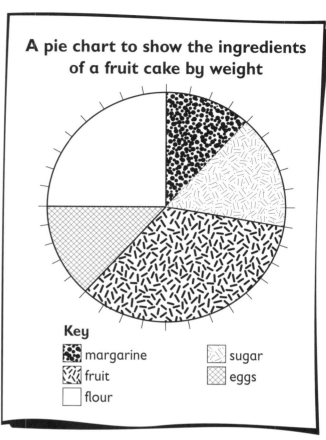

A pie chart to show the ingredients of a fruit cake by weight

Key
margarine   sugar
fruit   eggs
flour

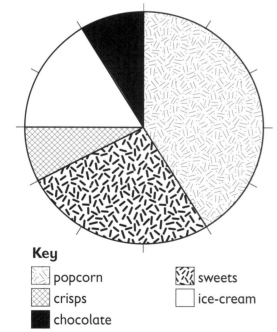

A pie chart to show which snacks were chosen at the cinema

Key
popcorn   sweets
crisps   ice-cream
chocolate

4 24 children went to the cinema. What fraction had:
  a popcorn? _____
  b sweets? _____
  c crisps? _____
  d ice-cream? _____
  e chocolate? _____

5 How many children had:
  a popcorn? _____
  b sweets? _____
  c crisps? _____
  d ice-cream? _____
  e chocolate? _____

Teachers' note Ensure that the children understand the concept of proportion. Also check that they understand that a pie chart shows the size of one piece of data in relation to the whole, for example in the first pie chart, the sector for margarine shows the weight of the margarine compared to the weight of all the ingredients, and how one piece of data can be seen in the context of the whole.

100% New Developing Mathematics
Handling Data: Ages 10–11
© A & C BLACK

Hot 'n' tasty: 1

Tom sells hot pies at local markets. The pie charts on Hot 'n' tasty: 2 show what pies were sold and the number sold in total at each stall.

1 Find pairs of stalls where the same number of pies were sold, and explain your answer.

a Fruity pie $\boxed{A}$ and $\boxed{E}$

On A, $\frac{3}{12}$ of 12 = 3. On E, $\frac{1}{12}$ of 36 = 3.

b Meaty pie $\boxed{}$ and $\boxed{}$

_____

c Veggie pie $\boxed{}$ and $\boxed{}$

_____

d Cheesy pie $\boxed{}$ and $\boxed{}$

_____

2 Overall, which pie do you think was:

  a the most popular? _____

  b the least popular? _____

3 On the back of this sheet, write two questions about the data for a partner to answer.

Teachers' note Use in conjunction with page 45, Hot 'n' tasty: 2. Each pie chart is divided into the same number of parts, but the total number of pies represented by each chart is different. Therefore, sectors that look the same size represent different numbers of pies. Model strategies to calculate the value of each sector of the pie charts. Calculators could be provided.

100% New Developing Mathema[t]
Handling Data: Ages 10–11
© A & C BLACK

Hot 'n' tasty: 2

Key

 Fruity   Meaty   Veggie   ☐ Cheesy

Stall A: 12 pies sold in total

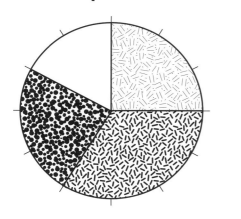

Stall B: 48 pies sold in total

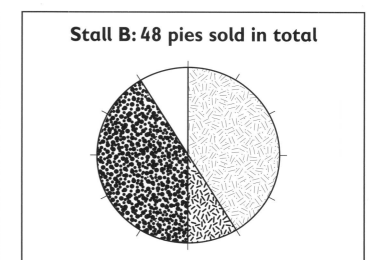

Stall C: 60 pies sold in total

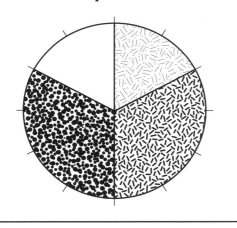

Stall D: 24 pies sold in total

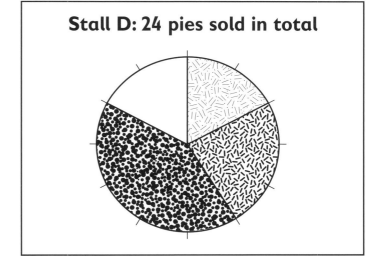

Stall E: 36 pies sold in total

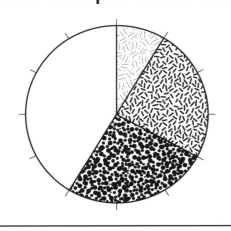

Stall F: 12 pies sold in total

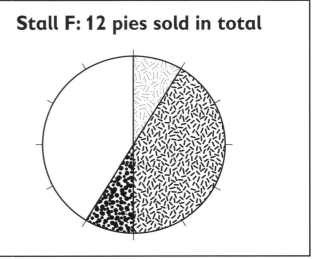

Teachers' note Use in conjunction with page 44, Hot 'n' tasty: 1.

100% New Developing Mathematics
Handling Data: Ages 10–11
© A & C BLACK

45

Plant sale: 1

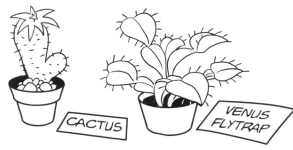

The pie charts on **Plant sale: 2** show the sales of plants each week for a month.

- **Use the pie charts to answer these questions.**

1 In week 1:

   a How many cacti were sold? _____

   b How many spider plants were sold? _____

2 In week 2, four orchids were sold.
What was the total number of plants sold during that week? _____

3 In week 3, twenty-four Venus flytraps were sold.
How many plants were sold in total during that week? _____

4 In week 4, how many more orchids than cacti were sold? _____

5 In which week were the most plants sold? _____

6 In which weeks were twelve orchids sold? _____

7 In which week were eight Venus flytraps sold? _____

8 How many spider plants were sold in total during the four weeks? _____

NOW TRY THIS!

- **The shop decides to sell only three types of plant. Which plant do you think they should stop selling, and why do you think this?** _____

_____

Teachers' note Use in conjunction with page 47, Plant sale: 2. Discuss how a pie chart is constructed and how the concept of proportion refers to parts of a whole, rather than specific numbers or values. Draw attention to the number of sectors into which the pie charts are divided and revise how concepts of division will help the children to answer the questions.

100% New Developing Mathema
Handling Data: Ages 10–11
© A & C BLACK

Plant sale: 2

Key

 Venus flytrap   cactus   spider plant   orchid

Week 1: 40 plants sold in total

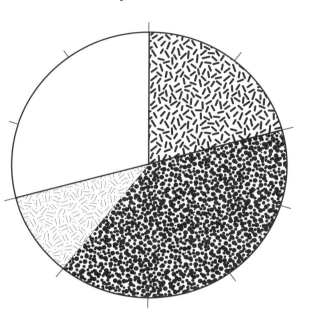

Week 2

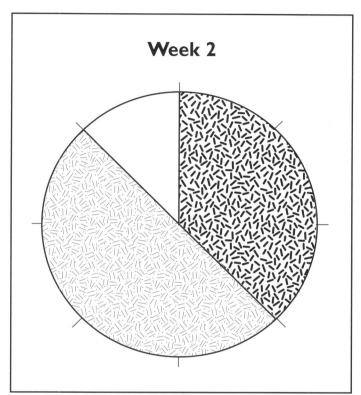

Week 3

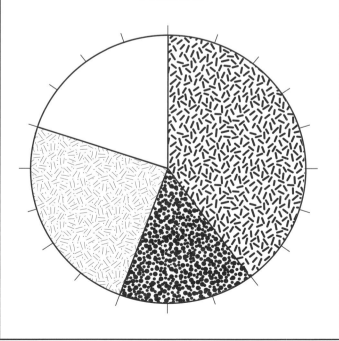

Week 4: 36 plants sold in total

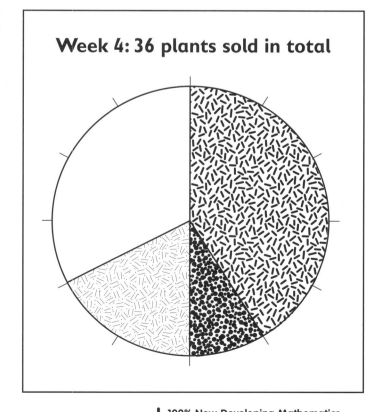

Teachers' note Use in conjunction with page 46, Plant sale: 1.

100% New Developing Mathematics
Handling Data: Ages 10–11
© A & C BLACK

Per 100 grams

You need a calculator.

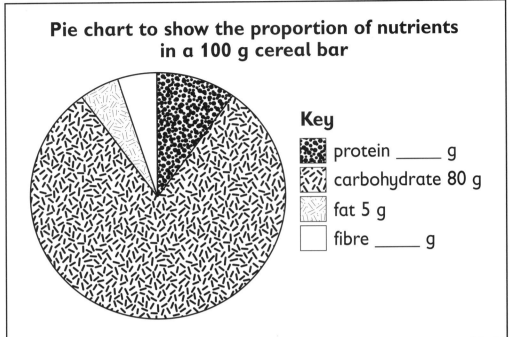

Pie chart to show the proportion of nutrients in a 100 g cereal bar

Key
protein _____ g
carbohydrate 80 g
fat 5 g
fibre _____ g

• **Use the pie chart to answer these questions.**

1 How many grams of fibre are there in the 100 g bar?
Write this in the key.

2 How many grams of protein are there in the 100 g bar?
Write this in the key.

3 Complete this table for cereal bars of different masses.

The proportion of nutrients for all the bars is the same as that of the 100 g bar.

Mass of bar	Protein	Carbohydrate	Fat	Fibre
200 g				
50 g				
120 g				
175 g				

NOW TRY THIS!

• **As a fraction, what proportion of fibre is in a cereal bar?** _____

Teachers' note Calculators should be available as the children work out how many grams would be in bars with different masses. During the plenary, discuss how the children used the pie chart to help them to work out the answers to questions 1 and 2, for example fibre is the same proportion as fat, so fibre is 5 g and protein is 10 g, since 100 g – 80 g – 5 g – 5 g = 10 g.

100% New Developing Mathema
Handling Data: Ages 10–11
© A & C BLACK

You need the digital cards cut from Home on the range: 2.

- I Shuffle the cards.
- I Turn over two cards and make a two-digit number.
- I Repeat until you have made five two-digit numbers.
- I Write the numbers in order in the circles, smallest to largest.
- I Calculate the **range** and write it in the square.

A ◯ ◯ ◯ ◯ ◯ ☐

- I Repeat to make six more sets of data.

Remember, the **range** is the difference between the highest and the lowest value in a set of data.

B ◯ ◯ ◯ ◯ ◯ ☐

C ◯ ◯ ◯ ◯ ◯ ☐

D ◯ ◯ ◯ ◯ ◯ ☐

E ◯ ◯ ◯ ◯ ◯ ☐

F ◯ ◯ ◯ ◯ ◯ ☐

G ◯ ◯ ◯ ◯ ◯ ☐

- • **Answer these questions about your data.**

1 Which set of data has the largest range? ____

2 Which set of data has the smallest range? ____

3 Why is the range useful? _____

_____

Teachers' note Use in conjunction with page 50, Home on the range: 2. The children could work in pairs for this activity. Once a set of numbers has been made, the digit cards are replaced and shuffled on the table. As an extension, ask the children to work out the missing number for this set of data, where the range is 74: 6, 32, 55, 70, (80).

100% New Developing Mathematics
Handling Data: Ages 10–11
© A & C BLACK

0

5

1

6

7

2

8

3

9

4

Teachers' note Use in conjunction with page 49, Home on the range: 1. The sheet could be printed onto card and laminated to provide a useful classroom resource.

100% New Developing Mathem
Handling Data: Ages 10–11
© A & C BLACK

Different modes: 1

• Find the **mode** for each set of data below and on **Different modes: 2.**

and on Different modes: 2.

The **mode** is the category that appears the most.

Tally chart to show pets owned by 6W

Pet	Tally
rabbit	IIII
dog	HHT HHT IIII
cat	HHT HHT HHT II
hamster	HHT HHT I
tortoise	I

Mode = _____

Bar chart to show favourite colours in 6W

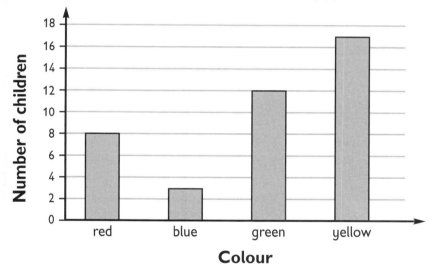

x-axis: Colour (red, blue, green, yellow)
y-axis: Number of children (0–18)

Mode = _____

Bar chart to show vehicles passing the playground

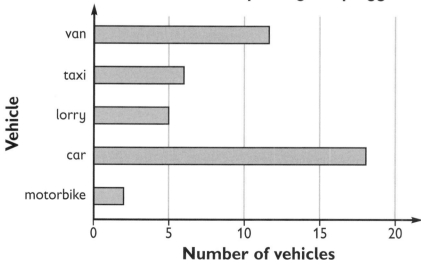

y-axis: Vehicle (van, taxi, lorry, car, motorbike)
x-axis: Number of vehicles (0–20)

Mode = _____

Teachers' note Use in conjunction with page 52, Different modes: 2. This activity consolidates the concept of the mode as an average. At the start of the lesson, ask the children to remind each other what the mode is and ask them to give examples for their class, for example the mode for the colour of socks is white.

**100% New Developing Mathematics
Handling Data: Ages 10–11
© A & C BLACK**

Different modes: 2

Pie chart to show favourite fruit in 6K

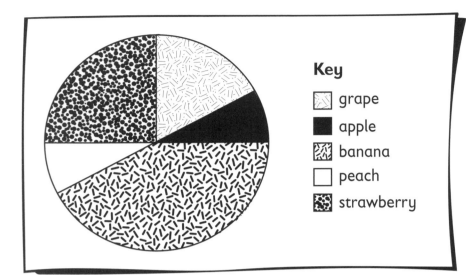

Key
- ▨ grape
- ■ apple
- ▨ banana
- □ peach
- ▨ strawberry

Mode = _____

Birds seen on a nature walk

We saw these birds:
robin, blackbird, thrush, robin, crow,
sparrow, blackbird, robin, sparrow,
sparrow, crow, sparrow, blackbird

Mode = _____

Table of test scores

Name	Test score
Amy	4
Ben	5
Ella	5
Callam	7
Eddie	9
Alia	6
George	3
Deepak	4
Isabel	6
James	5
Chloe	10

Mode = _____

Teachers' note Use in conjunction with page 51, Different modes: 1.

100% New Developing Mathem
Handling Data: Ages 10–11
© A & C BLACK

Paul's pool party

- **Paul invited his friends to his birthday pool party.**
- **Find the** | mean | **of each set of data about the swimming pool.**

The mean is the sum of all the data divided by the number of pieces of data.

Water toys in the pool			
Floats: 12	Balls: 25	Giant inflatable animals: 1	Inflatable rings: 14

1 The mean number of water toys is _____ .

Ages of people at the party														
5	7	7	8	10	10	10	10	10	10	10	10	11	11	21

2 The mean age of people at the party is _____ .

Temperature of children's pool in °C				
8 am: 25·5 °C	9 am: 25·7 °C	10 am: 26·2 °C	11 am: 26·6 °C	12 noon: 26 °C

3 The mean temperature of the pool is _____ °C.

Number of children in swimming lessons with Mr Splash				
Mon: 12	Tues: 5	Wed: 10	Thurs: 20	Fri: 8

4 The mean number of children in a swimming lesson is _____ .

Number of people in the pools in the morning		
Main pool: 35	Children's pool: 11	Splash pool: 2

5 The mean number of people in the pools is _____ .

- **Do you think that the mean for this data is helpful?**

Discuss your ideas with a partner.

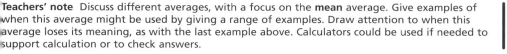

Teachers' note Discuss different averages, with a focus on the **mean** average. Give examples of when this average might be used by giving a range of examples. Draw attention to when this average loses its meaning, as with the last example above. Calculators could be used if needed to support calculation or to check answers.

100% New Developing Mathematics
Handling Data: Ages 10–11
© A & C BLACK

In the middle: 1

Craig asked his friends some questions.
The data he collected is shown below and on
In the middle: 2.

- Find the median for each set of data.
  To do this, write the data in order and
  then draw a ring around the middle value.

> The **median** is the middle value once a set of data has been ordered.

- ## What size feet do you have?

  5,   3,   4,   5,   3·5,   4,   4·5,   4·5,   5,   5·5,   5,   4,   3·5

- ## How old are you in years and months?

  10y 2m,   10y 5m,   10y 4m,   10y 2m,   10y 3m,   10y 4m,   10y 6m,

  10y 3m,   10y 5m

NOW TRY THIS!

- **On the back of this sheet, write seven numbers from 0 to 100. Make 43 the median.**

Teachers' note Use in conjunction with page 55, In the middle: 2. Give examples of when the median is useful. The children could collect data from others in the class, linked to the questions above, and use it to find the range, median, mode and mean.

100% New Developing Mathem
Handling Data: Ages 10–11
© A & C BLACK

In the middle: 2

- Find the median for each set of data below, by putting the data in order and then drawing a ring around the middle value.

- **How many brothers and sisters do you have?**

0, 1, 3, 2, 1, 0, 1, 1, 3, 2, 1, 2, 1, 0, 4

- **What is your favourite number between 1 and 20?**

14, 2, 4, 11, 19, 2, 18, 16, 15, 13, 12, 2, 17, 8, 3, 9, 5

NOW TRY THIS!

- **Choose one of Craig's questions.**
- **Ask people in your class this question and collect the data.**
- **Find the median for your data.**

Teachers' note Use in conjunction with page 54, In the middle: 1.

100% New Developing Mathematics
Handling Data: Ages 10–11
© A & C BLACK

Best average

- **Calculate the mean, median and mode for each set of data.**
- **Ring the average that you think is the best, and explain why.**

1 Computer game scores

58 38 47 44 38

mean ☐ median ☐ mode ☐

Explanation: _____

_____

_____

_____

2 Number of pets owned

2, 3, 1, 0, 5, 1, 4, 11, 2, 3, 1

mean ☐ median ☐ mode ☐

Explanation: _____

_____

_____

_____

3 Shoe sizes

2, 5, 3, 4, 3, 5, 4, 6, 5, 5, 3, 4, 5

mean ☐ median ☐ mode ☐

Explanation: _____

_____

_____

_____

NOW TRY THIS!

Here are Sophie's scores in the weekly spelling test: 5, 7, 5, 6, 8

- **Which average do you think she would give as her average score?**

Explain your choice to a partner.

Teachers' note In this activity, the children calculate each average for the same set of data. The focus is on evaluating which average is the best one to use in each situation. The children could discuss this in pairs. Question 3 involves a decimal average: provide calculators, if necessary, and remind the children how to record to one decimal place.

100% New Developing Mathema
Handling Data: Ages 10–11
© A & C BLACK

Side orders

These side orders were taken at Cath's Café.

	Mon	Tues	Wed	Thurs	Fri	Sat	Sun
Onion rings	4	9	3	0	3	7	11
Garlic bread	5	8	2	7	5	7	4
Chips	12	17	7	16	12	11	15
Green salad	8	6	4	7	7	10	14
Mixed peppers	9	11	3	11	8	16	15

- **Calculate the range, mean, median and mode for each food item.**

	Range	Mean	Median	Mode
Onion rings				
Garlic bread				
Chips				
Green salad				
Mixed peppers				

1 Which food item has a median of 7? _____

2 Which food item has a mode of 11? _____

3 Which food item has a mean of 8? _____

4 a Which food item should Cath definitely serve? _____

   b Why do you think so? _____

_____

5 a Which food item could Cath stop serving? _____

   b Why do you think so? _____

_____

Teachers' note Ask the children to give simple definitions of the range, mean, median and mode before starting this activity. Talk about the layout of the data and discuss how the average for each item can be calculated across the week, or for each day. The children can use a calculator to find the mean averages. If necessary, revise how to record to one decimal place.

100% New Developing Mathematics
Handling Data: Ages 10–11
© A & C BLACK

Cheeky Chalky

Alice's dog, Chalky, has chewed her homework.

1 Fill in the missing numbers.

a 6, ⬡ , 11, 14, 12, 8, 7, 9, 11, 4, 6   mode = 11

b 19, 31, 34, 83, 2, 13, 72, ⬡ , 11   median = 31

c 5·6, 49·9, ⬡ , 23·2, 64, 34·5, 22·7, 12·4   range = 80

d 24, 13, 7, ⬡ , 39   mean = 20

e 4, 7, 13, 3, 11, 2, 5, ⬡ , 15, 11, ⬡   mode = 7

f ⬡ , 64, 8, 32, ⬡ , 16, 2   median = 16

g 3, ⬡ , 2, 4, 6, ⬡ , 1   mean = 3

1 Which set of data has:
a the largest range? ____   **b** the smallest range? ____

3 On the back of this sheet, write two questions about the data for a partner to answer.

NOW TRY THIS!

• **Ring the two sets of data that have the same range.**

6, 2, 3, 7, 9, 1   3, 9, 6, 7, 12   2, 5, 14, 3, 7   16, 10, 8

Teachers' note Ensure that the children have a secure understanding of the range, mean, median and mode. Model how to find a missing answer. Calculators could be used to check answers. As a further extension, the children could make up their own data and ask others to find the missing value.

100% New Developing Mathema
Handling Data: Ages 10–11
© A & C BLACK

Cube collection

How many cubes do you think you can pick up in one hand?

- In your group, take three turns each.
- Record the results in this table.

Work in a group of five.

You need a copy of this worksheet each....

...and some cubes.

Name	1st turn	2nd turn	3rd turn

1 a Which average will you use for your score? _____

  b Why would you choose this average? _____

_____

2 Calculate the median, mean and mode for your scores.
median ____ mean ____ mode ____

3 a What Is the median, mean and mode for your group?
  median ____ mean ____ mode ____

  b How do these compare with other groups' averages?

4 Which is the fairest 'average' to use?

Discuss your ideas with your group.

NOW TRY THIS!

Hanif picked up these numbers of cubes: 8, 7, 9.

The median and the mean are the same.

- **Do you agree with his statement?**
- **Explain your answer to a partner.**

Teachers' note Each group will need interlocking cubes (or other cubes all of the same size). The children should consider which average they might want to use, as well as thinking about which average is most representative of their results. Calculators could be made available for calculating the averages for the group data.

**100% New Developing Mathematics
Handling Data: Ages 10–11
© A & C BLACK**

Beijing 2008

These are the results of the Men's 100 metre sprint at the Beijing Olympics. The race took place on 16th August, 2008.

Surname of athlete	Country	Date of birth	Result
Thompson	Trinidad/Tobago	07.06.85	9.89 sec
Powell	Jamaica	23.11.82	9.95 sec
Burns	Trinidad/Tobago	07.01.83	10.01 sec
Bolt	Jamaica	21.08.86	9.69 sec
Martina	Netherland Antilles	03.07.84	9.93 sec
Patton	United States	04.12.77	10.03 sec
Frater	Jamaica	06.10.82	9.97 sec
Dix	United States	31.01.86	9.91 sec

1 Who won: **a** Gold? _____ **b** Silver? _____

c Bronze? _____

2 How much faster was the athlete who won gold than the athlete who won silver? _____ sec

3 What is the mean time (to two decimal places) of the athletes? _____ sec

4 What is the difference in time between the athlete who won gold and the mean time? _____ sec

5 What is the median time? _____ sec

6 What was the age of:

a the oldest athlete? _____ years _____ months

b the youngest athlete? _____ years _____ months

7 What is the range of the athletes' ages? _____ years _____ months

NOW TRY THIS!

• **Which athlete's time was nearest to the mean time?** _____

Teachers' note Discuss the data to ensure that the children understand the headings. Calculators should be made available for this activity. Extension work could include children asking further questions about the data and researching other data from the most recent Olympic Games.

100% New Developing Mathema
Handling Data: Ages 10–11
© A & C BLACK

Blank line graph

Title _____

Teachers' note You could add a title and labels for the axes, or you could ask the children to complete these themselves.

100% New Developing Mathematics
Handling Data: Ages 10–11
© A & C BLACK

Blank spinners

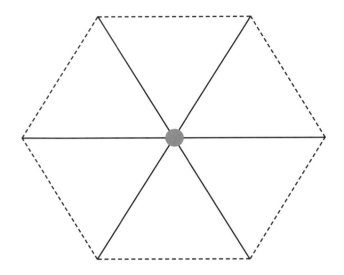

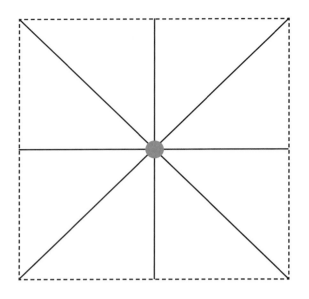

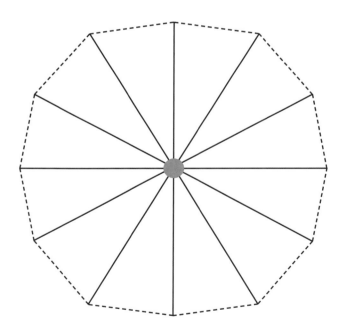

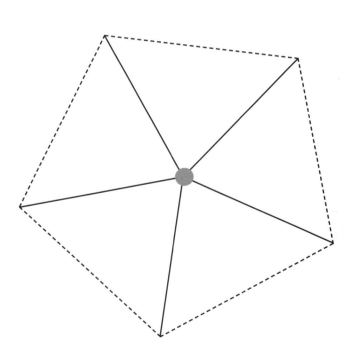

Teachers' note This template can be used to support work on chance and likelihood. The spinners can be deleted/copied and reproduced from the resource on the CD-ROM before printing to support differentiation. Copy onto card and cut out. The centre dot marks the position of a hole through which a pencil should be inserted to allow the card to spin.

100% New Developing Mathema **Handling Data: Ages 10–11** © **A & C BLACK**

Answers

p 13

The starred answers are suggestions only as it is up to the children to decide how likely Mr Perry is to stick precisely to the timetable.

Impossible	Very unlikely	Unlikely	Very likely	Certain
C	E		B*	A
G	F		D*	
			H*	

Now try this!

Check that the answers that the children give are shown in the timetable or are very close to the times shown in the timetable.

p 15

1 a <u>knight</u> or a <u>queen</u>   **b** a rook or a <u>white piece</u>
c a <u>pawn</u> or a <u>black piece</u>   **d** a <u>black piece</u> or a bishop
e a <u>knight</u> or a <u>rook</u>   **f** a white king or a <u>black rook</u>

2 Check individual answers.

3 a pawn
b Because there are more pawns on the board than any other type of chess piece.

Now try this!

The girl is right. There is the same number of kings as queens so Sam is equally likely to pick a king as a queen.

p 17

1 A   **2** A
3 a false   **b** false   **c** false
4 a fifty-fifty chance   **b** unlikely   **c** unlikely   **d** fifty-fifty chance

Now try this!

Neither, they are both equally likely.

p 18

A There should be more sections shaded black than criss-cross.
B There should be more sections dotted than left white.
C All sections should be dotted.
D There should be the same number of sections coloured green as red.
E There should be no sections coloured red.
F There should be at least three sections coloured blue.
G There should be two sections coloured green.
H There should be no sections coloured green or left white.

p 21

The answers for this activity will depend upon on the children's ideas. The easiest investigation is that in question C, because it uses data that is already known.

p 22

The answers will be based on the children's ideas, which can be linked to science and geography. Check that the children's ideas will lead to data being collected and represented fairly.

p 23

1 3   **2** 17
3 The results show that this girls' team performed better than this boys' team. To be able to say in general whether girls are better than boys at football, you need more information.

p 24

1 Classes 2, 5 and 6   **2** £72
3 The pie chart shows that Class 4 raised the most money. This might be because it is best at sport, but it might be because more people sponsored the children or people paid more money each time.

4 Again, the pie chart shows that Class 4 raised the most money. This might be because it cares most about charity, but it might be because more people sponsored the children or people paid more money each time or Class 4 are better at sport.

p 25

1 July and August   **2** 3 °C   **3** March   **4** 80 mm
5 The graphs only show the results for one year. You would need to look at the results from many more years to say whether London or Rome has more rain each year.
6 The graphs do seem to show this but you would need the results for other years to be able to say whether this is true or not.

p 27

1 Mike
2 a fewer   **b** 7
3 Because of cold and dark conditions with no Christmas presents or January sales.
4 The shop could have been closed whilst Spike was on holiday, or for refurbishment.
5 a Mike   **b** 970

Now try this!

April.

p 28

1 a Spike   **b** Because a higher number of bikes were sold.
2 17   **3 a** Mike   **b** 420
4 The children should refer to: varying number of daylight hours during the year; sales and promotions.

p 29

Frequencies for the week:
Grated carrot 57   Sweetcorn 26   Lettuce 48
Beetroot 49   Mixed pepper 66   Cucumber 52
1 mixed pepper
2 49   **3** sweetcorn   **4** Tuesday   **5 a** sweetcorn   **b** Thursday
6 caterers/suppliers

Now try this!

The statement is true. 60 portions of salad were served on Friday.

p 30

	Hammers	Glue guns	Hand drills	Saws
Reception	0	0	0	0
Year 1	6	0	0	10
Year 2	0	0	0	0
Year 3	15	0	4	0
Year 4	0	0	0	0
Year 5	12	5	8	10
Year 6	4	7	11	10

Now try this!

saws 0, glue guns 3, hammers 0, hand drills 0.

p 31

1 4   **2** 8   **3** 31   **4** no

Now try this!

£1205.

p 34

0–400 points	401–800 points	801–1200 points	1201–1600 points	1601–2000 points
Amy	Ella	Freya	Meena	Terri
Billy	Alfie	Harry		Ruby
Ajit				

Now try this!
lowest score: 801   highest score: 1200

p 36
1 8·5 cm   **2** 12·5 cm   **3** 9·75 cm

Now try this!
B

p 38
1 6:00 am   **2** The sun was setting.   **3** between 1:00 pm and 2:00 pm
4 A light was switched on and then off again.
5 a late spring or early summer
   b Because the sun rises early and sets late.

Now try this!
7 hours

p 40
3 2·15 m (accept answers from 2·1 m to 2·2 m)
4 1 year 8 months (accept answers from 1 year 7 months to 1 year 9 months)

Now try this!
a 1·7 m   **b** 17 m

p 42
(Accept answers + 1 those given.)
1 a 80 km   **b** 160 km   **c** 16 km   **d** 100 km   **e** 56 km
2 a 25 miles **b** 75 miles **c** 59 miles **d** 3 miles   **e** 93 miles
3 a 1·6 km   **b** 0·6 miles

Now try this!
Divide each by 50

p 43
1 a 5   **2 a** fruit   **b** margarine
3 a 40 g   **b** 60 g   **c** 120 g   **d** 50 g   **e** 90 g
4 a $\frac{5}{12}$ **b** $\frac{3}{12}$ or $\frac{1}{4}$ **c** $\frac{1}{12}$ **d** $\frac{2}{12}$ or $\frac{1}{6}$ **e** $\frac{1}{12}$
5 a 10   **b** 6   **c** 2   **d** 4   **e** 2

p 44
1 a A and E   On A, $\frac{3}{12}$ of 12 = 3. On E, $\frac{1}{12}$ of 36 = 3.
   b A and B   On A, $\frac{4}{12}$ of 12 = 3. On B, $\frac{1}{12}$ of 48 = 4.
   c B and C   On B, $\frac{5}{12}$ of 48 = 20. On C, $\frac{4}{12}$ of 60 = 20.
   d B and D   On B, $\frac{1}{12}$ of 48 = 4. On D, $\frac{2}{12}$ of 24 = 4.
2 a Veggie   **b** Cheesy

p 46
1 a 16   **b** 4   **2** 32   **3** 60   **4** 9   **5** week 3
6 weeks 1, 3 and 4   **7** week 1   **8** 41

Now try this!
Cacti, because proportionally fewer of these are sold and in week 2, no cacti were sold.

p 48
1 5 g
2 10 g
3

Mass of bar	Protein	Carbohydrate	Fat	Fibre
200 g	20 g	160 g	10 g	10 g
50 g	5 g	40 g	2·5 g	2·5 g
120 g	12 g	96 g	6 g	6 g
175 g	17·5 g	140 g	8·75 g	8·75 g

Now try this!
$\frac{1}{20}$

p 49
3 The range shows whether the data is all similar in size or whether it is spread out.

p 51
cat   yellow   car

p 52
banana   sparrow   5

p 53
1 13   **2** 10   **3** 26 °C   **4** 11   **5** 16

p 54
4·5 should be ringed.   10y 4m should be ringed.

Now try this!
Check that the fourth number is 43.

p 55
1 should be ringed.   11 should be ringed.

p 56
1 mean 45, median 44, mode 38. The mean, as it is between all the scores.
2 mean 3, median 2, mode 1. The median, as it shows that half the people own few or no pets.
3 mean 4·2, median 4, mode 5. The median, as most people asked have a shoe size that is about this size – only one has size 2 and one size 6.

Now try this!
The score that Sophie would be most likely to choose is the mean, as this has the highest value.

p 57

	Range	Mean	Median	Mode
Onion rings	11	5·3	4	3
Garlic bread	6	5·4	5	5,7
Chips	10	12·9	12	12
Green salad	10	7·9	7	7
Mixed peppers	13	10·4	11	11

1 green salad   **2** mixed peppers   **3** green salad
4 Check answers are reasonable.   **5** Check answers are reasonable.

p 58
1 a 11   **b** a number ≥ 31   **c** 85·6   **d** 17   **e** 7, 7
f one number ≤ £ 16 and one number ≥ 16
g any two numbers which total 5
2 a c   **b** g

Now try this!
6,2,3,7,9,1 and 16, 10, 8 should be ringed.

p 60
1 a Bolt   **b** Thompson   **c** Dix   **2** 0.20 seconds   **3** 9.92 seconds
4 0.23 seconds   **5** 9.94 seconds (middle two times added and divided by 2)   **6 a** 30 years 8 months   **b** 21 years 11 months   **7** 8 years 9 months

Now try this!
Martina (As the mean time is actually more than 9.92 seconds, it is nearer to 9.93 seconds than to 9.91 seconds.)